NOTES
POCKET

Personal details

Name

Address

Postcode

📞 Home

📞 Mobile

Email

In case of emergency contact:

Name

📞 Tel.

Contents

Year planner 2017

January		
1	Sun	
2	Mon	BANK HOLIDAY
3	Tue	BANK HOLIDAY SCOTLAND
4	Wed	
5	Thu	
6	Fri	
7	Sat	
8	Sun	
9	Mon	
10	Tue	
11	Wed	
12	Thu	
13	Fri	
14	Sat	
15	Sun	
16	Mon	
17	Tue	
18	Wed	
19	Thu	
20	Fri	
21	Sat	
22	Sun	
23	Mon	
24	Tue	
25	Wed	
26	Thu	
27	Fri	
28	Sat	
29	Sun	
30	Mon	
31	Tue	

February		
1	Wed	
2	Thu	
3	Fri	
4	Sat	
5	Sun	
6	Mon	
7	Tue	
8	Wed	
9	Thu	
10	Fri	
11	Sat	
12	Sun	
13	Mon	
14	Tue	
15	Wed	
16	Thu	
17	Fri	
18	Sat	
19	Sun	
20	Mon	
21	Tue	
22	Wed	
23	Thu	
24	Fri	
25	Sat	
26	Sun	
27	Mon	
28	Tue	

March		
1	Wed	
2	Thu	
3	Fri	
4	Sat	
5	Sun	
6	Mon	
7	Tue	
8	Wed	
9	Thu	
10	Fri	
11	Sat	
12	Sun	
13	Mon	
14	Tue	
15	Wed	
16	Thu	
17	Fri	BANK HOLIDAY N IRELAND
18	Sat	
19	Sun	
20	Mon	
21	Tue	
22	Wed	
23	Thu	
24	Fri	
25	Sat	
26	Sun	
27	Mon	
28	Tue	
29	Wed	
30	Thu	
31	Fri	

April		May		June	
1	Sat	1	Mon BANK HOLIDAY	1	Thu
2	Sun	2	Tue	2	Fri
3	Mon	3	Wed	3	Sat
4	Tue	4	Thu	4	Sun
5	Wed	5	Fri	5	Mon
6	Thu	6	Sat	6	Tue
7	Fri	7	Sun	7	Wed
8	Sat	8	Mon	8	Thu
9	Sun	9	Tue	9	Fri
10	Mon	10	Wed	10	Sat
11	Tue	11	Thu	11	Sun
12	Wed	12	Fri	12	Mon
13	Thu	13	Sat	13	Tue
14	Fri BANK HOLIDAY	14	Sun	14	Wed
15	Sat	15	Mon	15	Thu
16	Sun	16	Tue	16	Fri
17	Mon BANK HOLIDAY	17	Wed	17	Sat
18	Tue	18	Thu	18	Sun
19	Wed	19	Fri	19	Mon
20	Thu	20	Sat	20	Tue
21	Fri	21	Sun	21	Wed
22	Sat	22	Mon	22	Thu
23	Sun	23	Tue	23	Fri
24	Mon	24	Wed	24	Sat
25	Tue	25	Thu	25	Sun
26	Wed	26	Fri	26	Mon
27	Thu	27	Sat	27	Tue
28	Fri	28	Sun	28	Wed
29	Sat	29	Mon BANK HOLIDAY	29	Thu
30	Sun	30	Tue	30	Fri
		31	Wed		

Year planner 2017

July		August		September	
1	Sat	1	Tue	1	Fri
2	Sun	2	Wed	2	Sat
3	Mon	3	Thu	3	Sun
4	Tue	4	Fri	4	Mon
5	Wed	5	Sat	5	Tue
6	Thu	6	Sun	6	Wed
7	Fri	7	Mon BANK HOLIDAY SCOTLAND	7	Thu
8	Sat	8	Tue	8	Fri
9	Sun	9	Wed	9	Sat
10	Mon	10	Thu	10	Sun
11	Tue	11	Fri	11	Mon
12	Wed BANK HOLIDAY N IRELAND	12	Sat	12	Tue
13	Thu	13	Sun	13	Wed
14	Fri	14	Mon	14	Thu
15	Sat	15	Tue	15	Fri
16	Sun	16	Wed	16	Sat
17	Mon	17	Thu	17	Sun
18	Tue	18	Fri	18	Mon
19	Wed	19	Sat	19	Tue
20	Thu	20	Sun	20	Wed
21	Fri	21	Mon	21	Thu
22	Sat	22	Tue	22	Fri
23	Sun	23	Wed	23	Sat
24	Mon	24	Thu	24	Sun
25	Tue	25	Fri	25	Mon
26	Wed	26	Sat	26	Tue
27	Thu	27	Sun	27	Wed
28	Fri	28	Mon BANK HOLIDAY	28	Thu
29	Sat	29	Tue	29	Fri
30	Sun	30	Wed	30	Sat
31	Mon	31	Thu		

October	November	December
1 Sun	1 Wed	1 Fri
2 Mon	2 Thu	2 Sat
3 Tue	3 Fri	3 Sun
4 Wed	4 Sat	4 Mon
5 Thu	5 Sun	5 Tue
6 Fri	6 Mon	6 Wed
7 Sat	7 Tue	7 Thu
8 Sun	8 Wed	8 Fri
9 Mon	9 Thu	9 Sat
10 Tue	10 Fri	10 Sun
11 Wed	11 Sat	11 Mon
12 Thu	12 Sun	12 Tue
13 Fri	13 Mon	13 Wed
14 Sat	14 Tue	14 Thu
15 Sun	15 Wed	15 Fri
16 Mon	16 Thu	16 Sat
17 Tue	17 Fri	17 Sun
18 Wed	18 Sat	18 Mon
19 Thu	19 Sun	19 Tue
20 Fri	20 Mon	20 Wed
21 Sat	21 Tue	21 Thu
22 Sun	22 Wed	22 Fri
23 Mon	23 Thu	23 Sat
24 Tue	24 Fri	24 Sun
25 Wed	25 Sat	25 Mon BANK HOLIDAY
26 Thu	26 Sun	26 Tue BANK HOLIDAY
27 Fri	27 Mon	27 Wed
28 Sat	28 Tue	28 Thu
29 Sun	29 Wed	29 Fri
30 Mon	30 Thu	30 Sat
31 Tue		31 Sun

Useful numbers

Personal

Bank

Beautician

Building Society

Citizen's Advice citizensadvice.org.uk

    for England 03444 111 444

    for Wales 03444 77 20 20

Credit card emergency 1

Credit card emergency 2

Hairdresser

Life insurance policy number

    ☎ contact

    renewal date

Samaritans 116 123 (or local branch)

    samaritans.org

Solicitor

Work

Health

Blood group

Chemist

Chiropodist

Dentist

Doctor

Hospital

Medical insurance policy number

    ☎ contact

    renewal date

National insurance number

NHS (non-emergency) 111

    nhs.uk

NHS number

Optician

Notes

Home

Childminder/nursery

Council

Electrician

Electricity provider

Garage

Gas engineer

Gas provider

Home insurance policy number

  📞 contact

  renewal date

Plumber

Police (non-emergency) 101

  police.uk

School

TV licence renewal date

Vet

Water provider

Travel

Car insurance policy number

  📞 contact

  renewal date

Breakdown service

Driving licence number

MOT due date

Road tax renewal date

Service date

Vehicle registration number

Megabus 0900 1600 900 uk.megabus.com

National Express 0871 781 8181 nationalexpress.com

Eurostar 03432 186 186 eurostar.com

National Rail enquiries 0345 748 4950

  nationalrail.co.uk

Voyages-sncf 0844 848 5848 uk.voyages-sncf.com

Taxi

Passport adviceline 0300 222 0000

  gov.uk/passport-advice-line

Passport number

  renewal date

EHIC number/renewal date

Travel agent

Travel insurance policy number

  📞 contact

  renewal date

Personal contacts

Name

Address

📞 Telephone

    Mobile 1

    Mobile 2

    Work

Email 1

Email 2

Name

Address

📞 Telephone

    Mobile 1

    Mobile 2

    Work

Email 1

Email 2

Name

Address

📞 Telephone

    Mobile 1

    Mobile 2

    Work

Email 1

Email 2

Name

Address

📞 Telephone

    Mobile 1

    Mobile 2

    Work

Email 1

Email 2

Name

Address

📞 Telephone

    Mobile 1

    Mobile 2

    Work

Email 1

Email 2

Name

Address

📞 Telephone

    Mobile 1

    Mobile 2

    Work

Email 1

Email 2

Name

Address

📞 Telephone

   Mobile 1

   Mobile 2

   Work

Email 1

Email 2

Name

Address

📞 Telephone

   Mobile 1

   Mobile 2

   Work

Email 1

Email 2

Name

Address

📞 Telephone

   Mobile 1

   Mobile 2

   Work

Email 1

Email 2

Name

Address

📞 Telephone

   Mobile 1

   Mobile 2

   Work

Email 1

Email 2

Name

Address

📞 Telephone

   Mobile 1

   Mobile 2

   Work

Email 1

Email 2

Name

Address

📞 Telephone

   Mobile 1

   Mobile 2

   Work

Email 1

Email 2

Personal contacts

Name

Address

☎ Telephone

   Mobile 1

   Mobile 2

   Work

Email 1

Email 2

Name

Address

☎ Telephone

   Mobile 1

   Mobile 2

   Work

Email 1

Email 2

Name

Address

☎ Telephone

   Mobile 1

   Mobile 2

   Work

Email 1

Email 2

Name

Address

☎ Telephone

   Mobile 1

   Mobile 2

   Work

Email 1

Email 2

Name

Address

☎ Telephone

   Mobile 1

   Mobile 2

   Work

Email 1

Email 2

Name

Address

☎ Telephone

   Mobile 1

   Mobile 2

   Work

Email 1

Email 2

Name

Address

📞 Telephone

   Mobile 1

   Mobile 2

   Work

Email 1

Email 2

Name

Address

📞 Telephone

   Mobile 1

   Mobile 2

   Work

Email 1

Email 2

Name

Address

📞 Telephone

   Mobile 1

   Mobile 2

   Work

Email 1

Email 2

Name

Address

📞 Telephone

   Mobile 1

   Mobile 2

   Work

Email 1

Email 2

Name

Address

📞 Telephone

   Mobile 1

   Mobile 2

   Work

Email 1

Email 2

Name

Address

📞 Telephone

   Mobile 1

   Mobile 2

   Work

Email 1

Email 2

Personal contacts

Name

Address

☎ Telephone

   Mobile 1

   Mobile 2

   Work

Email 1

Email 2

Name

Address

☎ Telephone

   Mobile 1

   Mobile 2

   Work

Email 1

Email 2

Name

Address

☎ Telephone

   Mobile 1

   Mobile 2

   Work

Email 1

Email 2

Name

Address

☎ Telephone

   Mobile 1

   Mobile 2

   Work

Email 1

Email 2

Name

Address

☎ Telephone

   Mobile 1

   Mobile 2

   Work

Email 1

Email 2

Name

Address

☎ Telephone

   Mobile 1

   Mobile 2

   Work

Email 1

Email 2

Name

Address

📞 Telephone

  Mobile 1

  Mobile 2

  Work

Email 1

Email 2

Name

Address

📞 Telephone

  Mobile 1

  Mobile 2

  Work

Email 1

Email 2

Name

Address

📞 Telephone

  Mobile 1

  Mobile 2

  Work

Email 1

Email 2

Name

Address

📞 Telephone

  Mobile 1

  Mobile 2

  Work

Email 1

Email 2

Name

Address

📞 Telephone

  Mobile 1

  Mobile 2

  Work

Email 1

Email 2

Name

Address

📞 Telephone

  Mobile 1

  Mobile 2

  Work

Email 1

Email 2

2016

January
Mon		4	11	18	25
Tue		5	12	19	26
Wed		6	13	20	27
Thu		7	14	21	28
Fri	1	8	15	22	29
Sat	2	9	16	23	30
Sun	3	10	17	24	31

February
Mon	1	8	15	22	29
Tue	2	9	16	23	
Wed	3	10	17	24	
Thu	4	11	18	25	
Fri	5	12	19	26	
Sat	6	13	20	27	
Sun	7	14	21	28	

March
Mon		7	14	21	28
Tue	1	8	15	22	29
Wed	2	9	16	23	30
Thu	3	10	17	24	31
Fri	4	11	18	25	
Sat	5	12	19	26	
Sun	6	13	20	27	

April
Mon		4	11	18	25
Tue		5	12	19	26
Wed		6	13	20	27
Thu		7	14	21	28
Fri	1	8	15	22	29
Sat	2	9	16	23	30
Sun	3	10	17	24	

May
Mon		2	9	16	23	30
Tue		3	10	17	24	31
Wed		4	11	18	25	
Thu		5	12	19	26	
Fri		6	13	20	27	
Sat		7	14	21	28	
Sun	1	8	15	22	29	

June
Mon		6	13	20	27
Tue		7	14	21	28
Wed	1	8	15	22	29
Thu	2	9	16	23	30
Fri	3	10	17	24	
Sat	4	11	18	25	
Sun	5	12	19	26	

July
Mon		4	11	18	25
Tue		5	12	19	26
Wed		6	13	20	27
Thu		7	14	21	28
Fri	1	8	15	22	29
Sat	2	9	16	23	30
Sun	3	10	17	24	31

August
Mon	1	8	15	22	29
Tue	2	9	16	23	30
Wed	3	10	17	24	31
Thu	4	11	18	25	
Fri	5	12	19	26	
Sat	6	13	20	27	
Sun	7	14	21	28	

September
Mon		5	12	19	26
Tue		6	13	20	27
Wed		7	14	21	28
Thu	1	8	15	22	29
Fri	2	9	16	23	30
Sat	3	10	17	24	
Sun	4	11	18	25	

October
Mon		3	10	17	24	31
Tue		4	11	18	25	
Wed		5	12	19	26	
Thu		6	13	20	27	
Fri		7	14	21	28	
Sat	1	8	15	22	29	
Sun	2	9	16	23	30	

November
Mon		7	14	21	28
Tue	1	8	15	22	29
Wed	2	9	16	23	30
Thu	3	10	17	24	
Fri	4	11	18	25	
Sat	5	12	19	26	
Sun	6	13	20	27	

December
Mon		5	12	19	26
Tue		6	13	20	27
Wed		7	14	21	28
Thu	1	8	15	22	29
Fri	2	9	16	23	30
Sat	3	10	17	24	31
Sun	4	11	18	25	

2018

January
Mon	1	8	15	22	29
Tue	2	9	16	23	30
Wed	3	10	17	24	31
Thu	4	11	18	25	
Fri	5	12	19	26	
Sat	6	13	20	27	
Sun	7	14	21	28	

February
Mon		5	12	19	26
Tue		6	13	20	27
Wed		7	14	21	28
Thu	1	8	15	22	
Fri	2	9	16	23	
Sat	3	10	17	24	
Sun	4	11	18	25	

March
Mon		5	12	19	26
Tue		6	13	20	27
Wed		7	14	21	28
Thu	1	8	15	22	29
Fri	2	9	16	23	30
Sat	3	10	17	24	31
Sun	4	11	18	25	

April
Mon	2	9	16	23	30
Tue	3	10	17	24	
Wed	4	11	18	25	
Thu	5	12	19	26	
Fri	6	13	20	27	
Sat	7	14	21	28	
Sun	1	8	15	22	29

May
Mon		7	14	21	28
Tue	1	8	15	22	29
Wed	2	9	16	23	30
Thu	3	10	17	24	31
Fri	4	11	18	25	
Sat	5	12	19	26	
Sun	6	13	20	27	

June
Mon		4	11	18	25
Tue		5	12	19	26
Wed		6	13	20	27
Thu		7	14	21	28
Fri	1	8	15	22	29
Sat	2	9	16	23	30
Sun	3	10	17	24	

July
Mon		2	9	16	23	30
Tue		3	10	17	24	31
Wed		4	11	18	25	
Thu		5	12	19	26	
Fri		6	13	20	27	
Sat		7	14	21	28	
Sun	1	8	15	22	29	

August
Mon		6	13	20	27
Tue		7	14	21	28
Wed	1	8	15	22	29
Thu	2	9	16	23	30
Fri	3	10	17	24	31
Sat	4	11	18	25	
Sun	5	12	19	26	

September
Mon		3	10	17	24
Tue		4	11	18	25
Wed		5	12	19	26
Thu		6	13	20	27
Fri		7	14	21	28
Sat	1	8	15	22	29
Sun	2	9	16	23	30

October
Mon	1	8	15	22	29
Tue	2	9	16	23	30
Wed	3	10	17	24	31
Thu	4	11	18	25	
Fri	5	12	19	26	
Sat	6	13	20	27	
Sun	7	14	21	28	

November
Mon		5	12	19	26
Tue		6	13	20	27
Wed		7	14	21	28
Thu	1	8	15	22	29
Fri	2	9	16	23	30
Sat	3	10	17	24	
Sun	4	11	18	25	

December
Mon		3	10	17	24	31
Tue		4	11	18	25	
Wed		5	12	19	26	
Thu		6	13	20	27	
Fri		7	14	21	28	
Sat	1	8	15	22	29	
Sun	2	9	16	23	30	

2017

January

Mon		2	9	16	23	30
Tue		3	10	17	24	31
Wed		4	11	18	25	
Thu		5	12	19	26	
Fri		6	13	20	27	
Sat		7	14	21	28	
Sun	1	8	15	22	29	

February

Mon		6	13	20	27
Tue		7	14	21	28
Wed	1	8	15	22	
Thu	2	9	16	23	
Fri	3	10	17	24	
Sat	4	11	18	25	
Sun	5	12	19	26	

March

Mon		6	13	20	27
Tue		7	14	21	28
Wed	1	8	15	22	29
Thu	2	9	16	23	30
Fri	3	10	17	24	31
Sat	4	11	18	25	
Sun	5	12	19	26	

April

Mon		3	10	17	24
Tue		4	11	18	25
Wed		5	12	19	26
Thu		6	13	20	27
Fri		7	14	21	28
Sat	1	8	15	22	29
Sun	2	9	16	23	30

May

Mon	1	8	15	22	29
Tue	2	9	16	23	30
Wed	3	10	17	24	31
Thu	4	11	18	25	
Fri	5	12	19	26	
Sat	6	13	20	27	
Sun	7	14	21	28	

June

Mon		5	12	19	26
Tue		6	13	20	27
Wed		7	14	21	28
Thu	1	8	15	22	29
Fri	2	9	16	23	30
Sat	3	10	17	24	
Sun	4	11	18	25	

July

Mon		3	10	17	24	31
Tue		4	11	18	25	
Wed		5	12	19	26	
Thu		6	13	20	27	
Fri		7	14	21	28	
Sat	1	8	15	22	29	
Sun	2	9	16	23	30	

August

Mon		7	14	21	28
Tue	1	8	15	22	29
Wed	2	9	16	23	30
Thu	3	10	17	24	31
Fri	4	11	18	25	
Sat	5	12	19	26	
Sun	6	13	20	27	

September

Mon		4	11	18	25
Tue		5	12	19	26
Wed		6	13	20	27
Thu		7	14	21	28
Fri	1	8	15	22	29
Sat	2	9	16	23	30
Sun	3	10	17	24	

October

Mon		2	9	16	23	30
Tue		3	10	17	24	31
Wed		4	11	18	25	
Thu		5	12	19	26	
Fri		6	13	20	27	
Sat		7	14	21	28	
Sun	1	8	15	22	29	

November

Mon		6	13	20	27
Tue		7	14	21	28
Wed	1	8	15	22	29
Thu	2	9	16	23	30
Fri	3	10	17	24	
Sat	4	11	18	25	
Sun	5	12	19	26	

December

Mon		4	11	18	25
Tue		5	12	19	26
Wed		6	13	20	27
Thu		7	14	21	28
Fri	1	8	15	22	29
Sat	2	9	16	23	30
Sun	3	10	17	24	31

Calendar dates

UK holidays †

	2017	2018
New Year	Jan 2*	Jan 1
New Year (Scotland)	Jan 2/3*	Jan 1/2
St Patrick's Day (Northern Ireland)	Mar 17	Mar 19*
Good Friday	Apr 14	Mar 30
Easter Monday (except Scotland)	Apr 17	Apr 2
Early Spring	May 1	May 7
Spring	May 29	May 28
Battle of the Boyne (Northern Ireland)	Jul 12	July 12
Summer (Scotland)	Aug 7	Aug 6
Summer (except Scotland)	Aug 28	Aug 27
Christmas Day	Dec 25	Dec 25
Boxing Day	Dec 26	Dec 26

Notable dates

Burns' Night	Jan 25
Holocaust Memorial Day	Jan 27
Chinese New Year – Year of the Rooster	Jan 28
Accession of Queen Elizabeth II	Feb 6
St Valentine's Day	Feb 14
Shrove Tuesday (Pancake Day)	Feb 28
St David's Day (Wales)	Mar 1
Commonwealth Day	Mar 13
St Patrick's Day (Ireland)	Mar 17
Mothering Sunday	Mar 26
Birthday of Queen Elizabeth II	Apr 21
St George's Day (England)	Apr 23
World Red Cross/Red Crescent Day	May 8
Coronation Day	Jun 2
Queen's Official Birthday (t.b.c.)	Jun 10
Father's Day	Jun 18
Armed Forces' Day	Jun 24
St Swithin's Day	Jul 15
International Day of Peace	Sep 21
United Nations Day	Oct 24
Halloween	Oct 31
Armistice Day	Nov 11
Remembrance Sunday	Nov 12
Birthday of the Prince of Wales	Nov 14
St Andrew's Day (Scotland)	Nov 30

Religious dates

Christian

Epiphany	Jan 6
Ash Wednesday	Mar 1
Palm Sunday	Apr 9
Good Friday	Apr 14
Easter Day	Apr 16
Ascension Day	May 25
Whit Sunday, Pentecost	Jun 4
Trinity Sunday	Jun 11
Corpus Christi	Jun 15
Advent Sunday	Dec 3
Christmas Day	Dec 25

Buddhist

Parinirvana Day	Feb 8
Wesak (Buddha Day)	May 10
Bodhi Day (Buddha's enlightenment)	Dec 8

Hindu

Maha Shivaratri	Feb 25
Holi	Mar 13
Navaratri begins	Sep 21
Diwali begins (also celebrated by Sikhs)	Oct 19

Islamic

Ramadan begins	May 27
Eid Ul-Fitr	Jun 25
Eid Ul-Adha	Sep 1
Al-Hijra (New Year)	Sep 22
Milad un Nabi (Prophet's birthday)	Dec 1

Jewish

Purim begins	Mar 12
Pesach (Passover) begins	Apr 11
Shavuot (Pentecost) begins	May 31
Rosh Hashanah (Jewish New Year)	Sep 21
Yom Kippur (Day of Atonement)	Sep 30
Succoth (Tabernacles) begins	Oct 5
Chanukah begins	Dec 12

Sikh

These dates follow the Nanakshahi calendar

Birthday of Guru Gobind Singh	Jan 5
Vaisakhi	Apr 14
Birthday of Guru Nanak	Apr 15
Martyrdom of Guru Arjan Dev	Jun 16
Martyrdom of Guru Tegh Bahadur	Nov 24

Note: Many religious dates are based on the lunar calendar and, therefore, we cannot guarantee their accuracy.

†Bank Holiday dates can change *Substitute Bank Holidays – New Year's Day falls on a Sunday in 2017; St Patrick's Day falls on a Saturday in 2018.

Phases of the moon

● New moon				) First quarter		
	Day	H:M			Day	H:M
Jan	28	00:07		Jan	5	19:47
Feb	26	14:58		Feb	4	04:19
Mar	28	02:57		Mar	5	11:32
Apr	26	12:16		Apr	3	18:39
May	25	19:44		May	3	02:47
Jun	24	02:31		Jun	1	12:42
Jul	23	09:46		Jul	1	00:51
Aug	21	18:30		Jul	30	15:23
Sep	20	05:30		Aug	29	08:13
Oct	19	19:12		Sep	28	02:54
Nov	18	11:42		Oct	27	22:22
Dec	18	06:30		Nov	26	17:03
				Dec	26	09:20

○ Full moon				(Last quarter		
	Day	H:M			Day	H:M
Jan	12	11:34		Jan	19	22:13
Feb	11	00:33		Feb	18	19:33
Mar	12	14:54		Mar	20	15:58
Apr	11	06:08		Apr	19	09:57
May	10	21:42		May	19	00:33
Jun	9	13:10		Jun	17	11:33
Jul	9	04:07		Jul	16	19:26
Aug	7	18:11		Aug	15	01:15
Sep	6	07:03		Sep	13	06:25
Oct	5	18:40		Oct	12	12:25
Nov	4	05:23		Nov	10	20:36
Dec	3	15:47		Dec	10	07:51

Seasons

	Month	Day	H:M
Vernal equinox			
Spring begins	Mar	20	10:29
Summer solstice			
Summer begins	June	21	04:24
Autumnal equinox			
Autumn begins	Sep	22	20:02
Winter solstice			
Winter begins	Dec	21	16:28

British summertime

▶ Clocks go forward
1 hour at 1am on
26 March

◀ Clocks go back
1 hour at 2am on
29 October

Websites

bankholidaydates.co.uk

when-is.com

© Crown copyright and/or database rights. Reproduced with permission from HMNAO, UKHO and the Controller of Her Majesty's Stationery Office

Sunrise and sunset times Note: times vary – these are for London

Day	Rise H:M	Set H:M	Day	Rise H:M	Set H:M	Day	Rise H:M	Set H:M	Day	Rise H:M	Set H:M
January			**February**			**March**			**April**		
07	08:04	16:10	07	07:29	17:01	07	06:32	17:52	07	06:22	19:44
14	08:00	16:20	14	07:16	17:14	14	06:17	18:04	14	06:07	19:56
21	07:53	16:31	21	07:02	17:27	21	06:01	18:16	21	05:52	20:07
28	07:44	16:43	28	06:48	17:39	28	06:45	19:27	28	05:38	20:19
May			**June**			**July**			**August**		
07	05:21	20:34	07	04:45	21:14	07	04:53	21:18	07	05:34	20:38
14	05:10	20:45	14	04:43	21:19	14	05:00	21:12	14	05:45	20:25
21	05:00	20:55	21	04:43	21:22	21	05:09	21:04	21	05:56	20:10
28	04:53	21:04	28	04:46	21:22	28	05:18	20:55	28	06:07	19:55
September			**October**			**November**			**December**		
07	06:23	19:33	07	07:11	18:24	07	07:05	16:23	07	07:52	15:52
14	06:34	19:17	14	07:23	18:09	14	07:17	16:12	14	07:59	15:51
21	06:45	19:01	21	07:35	17:54	21	07:29	16:04	21	08:04	15:54
28	06:56	18:45	28	07:47	17:41	28	07:40	15:57	28	08:06	15:58

Height & weight chart

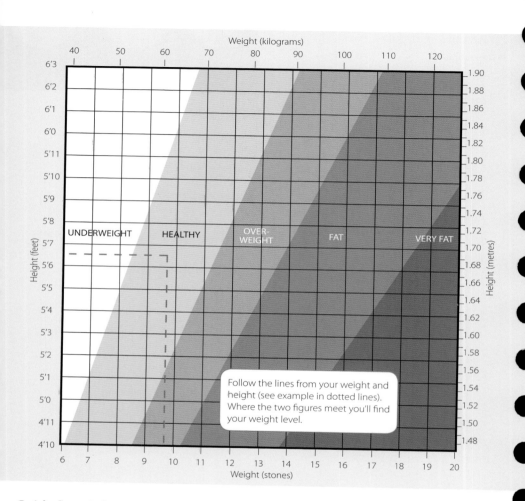

Weight (kilograms)
40 50 60 70 80 90 100 110 120

Height (feet) / Height (metres)

6'3 — 1.90
6'2 — 1.88
6'1 — 1.86
6'0 — 1.84
5'11 — 1.82 / 1.80
5'10 — 1.78
5'9 — 1.76
5'8 — 1.74
5'7 — 1.72 / 1.70
5'6 — 1.68
5'5 — 1.66
5'4 — 1.64 / 1.62
5'3 — 1.60
5'2 — 1.58
5'1 — 1.56 / 1.54
5'0 — 1.52
4'11 — 1.50
4'10 — 1.48

UNDERWEIGHT   HEALTHY   OVER-WEIGHT   FAT   VERY FAT

Weight (stones)
6 7 8 9 10 11 12 13 14 15 16 17 18 19 20

Follow the lines from your weight and height (see example in dotted lines). Where the two figures meet you'll find your weight level.

Guide for adult men and women

You may need to see your doctor if you are very underweight.

Desirable range for health.

Try to lose weight until you are in the desirable range.

To avoid potential health problems, it is important to lose weight.

Talk to your doctor or practice nurse. You can be referred to a dietitian.

Body Mass Index

To calculate your BMI, divide your weight in kilograms by your height in metres and then divide the answer by your height again. Alternatively, the NHS has an online BMI calculator (nhs.uk).

Below 18.5	underweight	**18.5–24.9**	healthy
25–29.9	overweight	**30 +**	obese

Metric conversions

Length

			To convert	multiply by
1 millimetre (mm)		= 0.0394in	mm to in	0.0394
1 centimetre (cm)	= 10mm	= 0.394in	cm to in	0.394
1 metre (m)	= 100cm	= 1.09yd	m to yd	1.09
1 kilometre (km)	= 1000m	= 0.621 mile	km to mi	0.621
1 inch (in)		= 2.54cm	in to cm	2.54
1 foot (ft)	= 12in	= 30.5cm	ft to cm	30.5
1 yard (yd)	= 3ft	= 0.914m	yd to m	0.914
1 mile (mi)	= 1760yd	= 1.61km	mi to km	1.61

Area

			To convert	multiply by
1 sq millimetre (mm)		= 0.00155sq in	mm^2 to in^2	0.00155
1 sq centimetre (cm)	= 100sq mm	= 0.155sq in	cm^2 to in^2	0.155
1 sq metre (m)	= 10,000sq cm	= 1.20sq yd	m^2 to yd^2	1.20
1 hectare (ha)	= 10,000sq m	= 2.47a	ha to a	2.47
1 sq kilometre (km)	= 100ha	= 0.386sq mile	km^2 to mi^2	0.386
1 sq inch (in)		= 6.45sq cm	in^2 to cm^2	6.45
1 sq foot (ft)	= 144sq in	= 0.0929sq m	ft^2 to m^2	0.0929
1 sq yard (yd)	= 9sq ft	= 0.836sq m	yd^2 to m^2	0.836
1 acre (a)	= 4840sq yd	= 4047sq m	a to m^2	4047
1 sq mile (mi)	= 640a	= 2.59sq km	mi^2 to km^2	2.59

Volume

			To convert	multiply by
1 cu centimetre (cm)	= 1000cu mm	= 0.0611cu in	cm^3 to in^3	0.0611
1 cu decimetre (dm)	= 1000cu cm	= 0.0353cu ft	dm^3 to ft^3	0.0353
1 cu metre (m)	= 1000cu dm	= 1.31cu yd	m^3 to yd^3	1.31
1 cu inch (in)		= 16.4cu cm	in^3 to cm^3	16.4
1 cu foot (ft)	= 1730cu in	= 28.4cu dm	ft^3 to dm^3	28.4
1 cu yard (yd)	= 27cu ft	= 0.765cu m	yd^3 to m^3	0.765

Capacity

			To convert	multiply by
1 millilitre (ml)		= 0.0352fl oz	ml to fl oz	0.0352
1 centilitre (cl)	= 10ml	= 0.352fl oz	cl to fl oz	0.352
1 litre (l)	= 100cl	= 1.76pt	l to pt	1.76
1 fluid ounce (fl oz)		= 28.4ml	fl oz to ml	28.4
1 gill (gi)	= 5fl oz	= 14.2cl	gi to cl	14.2
1 pint (pt)	= 20fl oz	= 0.568l	pt to l	0.568
1 quart (qt)	= 2pt	= 1.14l	qt to l	1.14
1 gallon (gal)	= 4qt	= 4.55l	gal to l	4.55

Weight

			To convert	multiply by
1 gram (g)	= 1000mg	= 0.0353oz	g to oz	0.0353
1 kilogram (kg)	= 1000g	= 2.20lb	kg to lb	2.20
1 tonne (t)	= 1000kg	= 0.984 ton	tonne to ton	0.984
1 ounce (oz)	= 438 grains	= 28.3g	oz to g	28.3
1 pound (lb)	= 16oz	= 0.454kg	lb to kg	0.454
1 stone (st)	= 14lb	= 6.35kg	st to kg	6.35
1 ton (t)	= 160st	= 1.02 tonne	ton to tonne	1.02

Cook's information

Dry weight conversions

grams (g)	ounces (oz)
15	½
25	1
50	2
75	3
110	4 (¼lb)
150	5
175	6
200	7
225	8 (½lb)
250	9
275	10
300	11
350	12 (¾lb)
375	13
400	14
425	15
450	16 (1lb)
500	1lb 2oz
680	1½lb
750	1lb 10oz
900	2lb

These quantities are not exact, but they have been calculated to give proportionately correct measurements.

Liquid conversions

millilitres (ml)	fluid ounces (fl oz)	US cups
15	½	1 tbsp (level)
30	1	⅛
60	2	¼
90	3	⅜
125	4	½
150	5 (¼ pint)	⅔
175	6	¾
225	8	1
300	10 (½ pint)	1¼
350	12	1½
450	16	2
500	18	2¼
600	20 (1 pint)	2½
900	1½ pints	3¾
1 litre	1¾ pints	1 quart (4 cups)
1.25 litres	2 pints	1¼ quarts
1.5 litres	2½ pints	3 US pints
2 litres	3½ pints	2 quarts

These quantities are not exact, but they have been calculated to give proportionately correct measurements.

Reference intake (RI)

Energy (calories)	2,000
Fat (g)	70
of which saturates (g)	20
Carbohydrate (g)	260
of which total sugars (g)	90
Protein (g)	50
Salt (g)	6

Spoon measures

1 tablespoon	=	3 level teaspoons
1 level tablespoon	=	15ml
1 level teaspoon	=	5ml

If greater accuracy is not required:

1 rounded teaspoon	=	2 level teaspoons
1 heaped teaspoon	=	3 level teaspoons or 1 level tablespoon

Grilling times: fish

	minutes each side
Cod (steak)	5–6
Dover sole (fillet)	2–3
Halibut (steak)	5–6
Herring (whole)	4–5
Mackerel (whole)	6–7
Monkfish (steak)	5–6
Plaice (whole)	4–6
Plaice (fillet)	2–3
Salmon (steak)	5–6
Skate	5–6
Tuna (steak)	1–2

Times given for fish weighing approximately 175–225g (6–8oz).

Oven temperatures

°C	(fan)	°F	gas	description
110	(90)	225	¼	cool
120/130	(100/110)	250	½	cool
140	(120)	275	1	very low
150	(130)	300	2	very low
160/170	(140/150)	325	3	low to mod
180	(160)	350	4	moderate
190	(170)	375	5	moderately hot
200	(180)	400	6	hot
220	(200)	425	7	hot
230	(210)	450	8	hot
240 (	220)	475	9	very hot

Guide to recommended equivalent settings, not exact conversions. Always refer to your cooker instruction book.

Roasting times: meat

Set oven temperature to 180°C/350°F/Gas 4.

	cooking time per 450g/1lb	extra cooking time
Beef		
rare	20 min	20 min
medium	25 min	25 min
well done	30 min	30 min
Lamb		
medium	25 min	25 min
well done	30 min	30 min
Pork		
medium	30 min	30 min
well done	35 min	35 min

Let the cooked meat rest for 5–15 minutes before carving to allow the juices to be reabsorbed and to make carving easier.

Steaming times: vegetables

	minutes
Asparagus	5–7
Beansprouts	3–4
Beetroot (sliced)	5–7
Broccoli (florets)	5–7
Brussels sprouts	5–7
Cabbage (chopped)	4–6
Carrots (thickly sliced)	5–7
Cauliflower (florets)	5–7
Courgettes (sliced)	3–5
Green beans	5–7
Leeks	5–8
Mangetout peas	3–5
Peas	3–5
Potatoes (cubed)	5–7

Times given are for steaming from when water has started to boil.

Roasting times: poultry

	oven temperature	cooking time per 450g/1lb	extra cooking time	resting time
Chicken	200°C/400°F/Gas 6	20 min	30 min	15 min
Turkey (stuffed weight)				
small (under 6kg/13lb)	200°C/400°F/Gas 6	12 min	20 min	30 min
large	180°C/350°F/Gas 4	16 min	—	30 min
Duck	200°C/400°F/Gas 6	35 min	—	15 min
	for 45 min then 180°C/350°F/Gas 4			

* Note that for fan ovens, cooking times are generally reduced by 10 minutes for every hour.

Clever cooking

No matter how much spare cash we may or may not have, no one likes to throw away food. Not only is it wasteful but it's damaging to the environment too.

If we all stopped wasting the food that could be eaten, the benefit to the planet would be the equivalent of taking one in four cars off the road. Luckily, cutting food waste is easy!

Great cooking begins with an organised kitchen and proper planning. This doesn't negate the chance for spontaneous dishes, but reduces food waste and ensures that all the ingredients required are at hand.

Forward planning

Before you do your weekly shop, plan your meals for the next five days. Check your fridge or freezer first to see what you can make use of.

Browse your recipes and write your chosen meals down on a noticeboard or list on the fridge. Then write your shopping list based on these meals (plus any other foods that you need for breakfast, lunch and snacks).

When you have eaten the first five meals look at what you have left in your fridge, freezer and cupboard and create your final two meals from leftovers. Don't forget to include opened jars and packets as well as fresh foods. Be creative!

Clever storage

Place items in your fridge with the shortest shelf-life at the front. Keep fresh food in the packet it came in – some use clever technology to prolong their shelf life. Be freezer-friendly; check use-by dates and anything you are unlikely to use before its date pop in the freezer (check its label and don't freeze if it's already been frozen).

Seal open packets with pegs or decant into storage jars to prevent them from drying out.

If you cook too much, allow to cool, pop into a freezer-proof tub, label and freeze. This works especially well for meals such as stews and curries, where it makes sense to batch-cook. To defrost, place the tub in the fridge overnight, then heat until piping hot in the microwave or on the hob.

Whizz dry bread in a food processor, seal in bags and freeze. Grate ginger, chop herbs and chillies and store in ice cube trays in the freezer.

Savvy shopping

Try to stick to your list. If you are tempted by multibuy offers make sure that you freeze anything that you are unlikely to use before its use-by date. If you often throw away fruit and veg, buy them loose rather than in large packs.

If you have a small household you can buy small portions of meat and fish from the meat/fish counter or from your local butcher/fishmonger. If you want to bulk-buy (which can be more economical) split your pack of meat/fish into portions, wrap well and freeze.

Grow your own herbs on your windowsill or by the back door in summer. A plentiful supply of fresh herbs is so useful and much cheaper than buying from the supermarket.

Creative cooking

Try to use what you already have before buying new ingredients. This encourages your creativity as well as reducing food waste:

Create amazing salads using leftover leaves, veg, fruit and nuts or seeds. For leafy salads make dressings using oils and vinegars with herbs or mustards. For crunchy salads, creamy dressings work well, using crème fraîche or mayonnaise.

Stir leftover cold meat or fish into pasta with pesto, crème fraîche or fromage frais. Or add to an omelette with herbs, cheese and vegetables.

All sorts of veg can be used in egg fried rice and leftover cured meats, such as chorizo or Parma ham, are a brilliant addition too.

Vegetables which are slightly past their best can be cooked in stock and whizzed with a stick blender for soup, which freezes brilliantly.

And last but not least, use almost anything to top a baked potato. Sometimes, simple food can be the best!

Now, enjoy perusing your recipes for new ideas and shop with a clear conscience.

Pot herbs for the kitchen

Fresh herbs give a great lift to many foods – so grow your own in pots sited near the kitchen for ease of picking. And why not choose some colourful, fun containers to plant in?

Sow seeds in March, or buy small herb plants in April or May, pot up at once and start picking leaves as soon as the plants have grown slightly.

This should only take about an hour.

What you need

Plants
Seed packets or small plants of parsley, thyme, marjoram, sage, mint and rosemary.

Equipment
- Six small plastic pots for potting up seedlings bought at the garden centre.
- Seed tray, modular cell system or jiffy pots for sowing seeds, if using.
- Five containers such as the enamel kettles and pots.
- Soil-based potting compost and proprietary seed compost if using.
- Broken crocks for drainage.
- Trowel.

Instructions

1 Fill the seed tray or modular cell system with seed compost and sow your seeds according to the instructions on the packets, or sow in jiffy pots according to the manufacturer's instructions. Keep on a kitchen windowsill while the seeds germinate, then move outside when all danger of frost is past.
2 When the seedlings are large enough to handle, transfer them into plastic pots using compost and lining with broken crocks for drainage.
3 Or, line the plastic pots with broken crocks and fill with potting compost, into which you have mixed some sharp sand (if using). Then plant your garden centre seedlings, place into the containers and set out in an attractive arrangement. Allow one herb per container, but if the container is big enough, put several in together – here rosemary, parsley and mint have been put in the central container.
4 Place the young herb plants outside only when all danger of frost is past. If you're uncertain, place them outside on sunny days and bring them in at night until the weather warms up enough for them to be left outside permanently.
5 Pick and use the leaves regularly. All these herbs can grow quite large and, by the end of summer, may well have outgrown their containers unless you keep them under control.

Notes

Most herbs do best in full sun. They don't require rich soil, but they must not be allowed to get waterlogged, so good drainage is essential. Rosemary, sage, thyme and marjoram are tough, shrubby plants and can be kept going for years if put into the ground or grown in large enough pots. Mint and parsley are herbaceous and will die down in winter, but reappear again in spring.

Aftercare

Regular picking is needed, and watering with care.

Tiny Tomatoes in Terracotta

The taste of a sun-warmed tomato picked straight from the bush is leagues removed from anything you can buy in a shop. Container-growing is easy and you are rewarded with a succession of tasty toms beyond compare.

Pot up young tomato plants in late spring or early summer when all danger from frost is past for cropping throughout the summer.

Planting four to six pots shouldn't take more than an hour.

What you need

Plants

Four to six (or more) young bush tomato plants – a wide range of different varieties is available from garden centres – including red, yellow and even purple ones. 'Red Alert', 'Pixie' and 'Tiny Tim' are all good small-fruited varieties with excellent flavour. 'Roma' is a plum-shaped variety.

Equipment

- Terracotta, plastic or ceramic pots with drainage holes in the bottom.
- Soil-based potting compost.
- Broken crocks for drainage.
- Trowel.
- Liquid tomato fertiliser.

Instructions

1 Line the containers with broken crocks for drainage. Three-quarters fill with potting compost.

2 Plant the tomatoes, one to a pot, firming them in well and topping up with more compost.

3 Place in a sunny, sheltered site – water well.

4 The tomato compost needs to be kept just moist at all times. Try to water regularly, little and often – an irregular regime could cause the tomatoes to split. Feed regularly with a liquid tomato fertiliser to ensure consistent development of the fruits.

Tips

As an alternative to pots, try raising tomatoes in growbags – the bags come complete with just the right soil conditions. You can grow bush or cordon varieties in growbags. Cordons needing staking and you have to pinch out side shoots.

Notes

For successful tomato growing in containers, make sure you buy an appropriate variety. Check that it is a bush variety AND check that it is suitable for outdoor cultivation – many are bred for growing in greenhouses and won't thrive outside. Take care, too, to choose as sunny and warm a site as possible.

Aftercare

Bush tomato varieties don't need any pinching out of side shoots. Pick the tomatoes as they ripen. If there are still some green tomatoes on the plants when frost seems likely, pick them all and bring them indoors to ripen.

Squeaky clean kitchen

Very few of us enjoy cleaning the kitchen but unfortunately it is something that has to be done.

There are literally hundreds of products on the market which claim to clean better and brighter than others. But are they really necessary?

Using too many chemicals in your home can damage your health, as well as your purse. These chemicals can be ingested and may also irritate your skin. Use some of these tips for a clean, fresh and healthy kitchen.

Cupboard doors: Clean with a microfibre cloth and a spray of white vinegar diluted with an equal amount of water and a few drops of essential oil.

Dishes: Wash dishes after each meal. Don't leave them to accumulate. If washing by handy always wash the cleanest items first, such as glasses and mugs, followed by plates and cutlery and then finally cookware.

Dishwasher: Empty and wash the filter, then pour a cup of white vinegar into the bottom. Run on empty on a normal cycle.

Drains: To clean and refresh, mix 3 heaped tablespoons of washing soda crystals with 4 litres (7 pints) of warm water. Pour this down the drain and follow with hot water.

If the drain is clogged pour 3 tablespoons of bicarbonate of soda down the plughole and then follow with 3 tablespoons of white vinegar. Leave for 5 minutes and then flush with plenty of hot water.

Floor: Regularly sweep and mop with hot, soapy water.

Food residue: To remove stubborn food from baking trays and roasting tins sprinkle with biological washing powder and add hot water. Leave to soak then wash as usual.

Cleaning kit

- Alka-Seltzer tablets
- Bicarbonate of soda
- Biological washing powder or detergent
- Concentrated washing-up liquid
- Denture tablets
- Essential oils (peppermint, lemon or eucalyptus)
- Lemon juice
- Olive oil

- Spray bottles
- Washing soda crystals
- White vinegar
- Salt
- Microfibre cloths, cut-up old t-shirt cloths and scouring pads
- Mop, bucket, brush, dustpan, old toothbrushes and bottlebrush

Using too many chemicals in your home can damage your health, as well as your purse.

Fragrance: Add a few drops of your favourite essential oil to the inside of the kitchen roll tube for a fresh fragrance.

Fridge, hob, oven and splash-back: Clean with a solution of 4 tablespoons of bicarbonate of soda mised with 1 litre (1 ¾ pints) of warm water.

Glass vase stain: To remove a stain from the bottom of a glass vase, fill with water and add two Alka-Seltzer tablets. If the vase is dirty and you cannot reach the bottom simply fill with hot soapy water, add a teaspoon of dry rice or lentils and shake vigorously.

Kettle: Add a couple of denture tablets with some water and leave overnight. Rinse well and any lime-scale should have disappeared.

Silver: Polish with lemon juice and then buff to a shine with a soft clean cloth.

Stainless steel: Use a tiny amount of olive oil on a cloth to clean appliances and then polish to a shine with a microfibre cloth.

Taps: Use an old toothbrush to clean the taps thoroughly and clean plugholes with an old bottle brush.

Tea and coffee stains: Remove from mugs by adding equal

amounts of salt and vinegar. Leave for a few minutes, remove with kitchen paper and then wash well.

Tiles: Remove grease from tiles with a spray of white vinegar diluted with an equal amount of water and a few drops of essential oil, then polish with a soft cloth.

Water marks: To remove from wood, rub with a little mayonnaise and then wipe clean with a damp cloth.

Windows: Clean with a few sprays of white vinegar and water solution (1 part vinegar to 9 parts water) and then buff dry with a paper towel.

Stain removal

The most important factor in attacking stains is to act swiftly. The newer the stain, whether greasy or non-greasy, or a combination of the two, the easier it will be to remove without damage.

Personal

Blood: Soak in biological detergent and cold water, or cold water with salt added, and wash in heavy-duty biological detergent. Or try rubbing a mixture of cornflour and cold water into the stain, leaving to dry and brushing off.

Collar and cuff dirt: Apply liquid biological detergent directly with an old toothbrush. Wash as usual.

Deodorant: Sponge with a hydrogen peroxide solution (see box); apply heavy-duty liquid detergent to the area; wash.

Perspiration: Dab with white vinegar solution (see box); leave for 5 minutes. Soak and wash in biological detergent.

Urine and vomit: Soak in biological detergent and cold water, and wash in heavy-duty biological detergent.

Foodstuffs

Egg, milk and gravy: Soak in biological detergent and cold water, and wash in heavy-duty biological detergent.

Chewing gum: Freeze to make the gum brittle, using an ice cube inside a plastic bag; scrape

it off, dab with methylated spirits (see box) and wash as usual.

Chocolate: Apply biological liquid detergent to the area; wash in heavy-duty detergent (containing bleach). On white items, soak in hydrogen peroxide solution (see box) and wash. Or soak in milk and wash in washing-up liquid; dab any remaining stain with white vinegar (see box), leave and wash as usual. Also good for coffee marks.

Oil/salad dressings: Sprinkle with cornflour to absorb grease, brush off, soak with washing-up liquid and then wash as normal.

Beverages

Tea, coffee, soft drinks: Soak in cool water, use a pre-wash treatment and wash in heavy-duty detergent (with bleach). Or use a hydrogen peroxide solution (see box) before washing.

Red wine: Mop up excess liquid and treat as for oil. Or cover stain with salt and leave for 30

What to do

■ Remove any solids with a blunt knife, and blot liquids with white kitchen paper.

■ Apply stain remover to a small, unseen area and wait 5–10 minutes. If the fabric reacts, seek dry-cleaning advice. Avoid treating delicate or expensive fabrics, or those that require dry-cleaning only.

■ Don't over-soak the fabric with a cleaning agent. To avoid making a ring mark, use a soft, absorbent cloth to apply the cleaning agent and work in a circular motion from the outside inwards. Dab, rather than rub, because rubbing can damage the fabric and it can also spread the stain.

Cleaning kit

Detergents
Biological and heavy-duty liquid detergents.

Eucalyptus oil
Available from essential oils section of major chemists.

Hydrogen peroxide
Ask your chemist for 20 volume strength. Mix 1 part to 6 parts water; soak item for 30 minutes or until the stain has cleared.

Lighter fluid
Apply neat with cotton wool.

Methylated spirits
Available from chemists. Apply with cotton-wool buds.

Pre-wash treatments
Some of these are formulated to treat a whole raft of common stains, some are more specific. Follow the instructions on the container.

White spirit
Dab neat on to grease stains.

White vinegar
Mix 15ml vinegar to 300ml water (3 tsp to ½ pint).

■ Chemical treatment may damage old or worn fabric.

■ Always test the fabric first in an inconspicuous area. If in doubt, take a stained garment to a dry-cleaner.

minutes. Sponge with a warm solution of biological detergent (with bleach), rinse with cold water and wash as normal. If the stain has dried, treat as for blood. On upholstery and carpets, blot with white kitchen paper. If it cannot be rinsed, spray with soda water, or white wine, then mop with kitchen paper.

White wine: Rinse with plenty of warm water, or treat as tea.

Grease, glue, wax, oil and tar

Oil, fat, grease and tar: Dab the area with eucalyptus oil; wash in water as hot as the fabric allows.

Glue: Try to remove glue before it sets; apply methylated spirits (see box) for natural fabrics, or lighter fluid for synthetic fabrics.

Wax crayons, cosmetics and shoe polish: Treat with white spirit (see box) to remove the wax stain. Apply a pre-wash

treatment and wash in heavy-duty detergent (with bleach).

Miscellaneous

Grass and mud: Dab on methylated spirits (see box) and rinse off with warm soapy water. Apply a pre-wash treatment and then wash in heavy-duty detergent (with bleach). For a new stain, try soaking in white vinegar (see box), or squeeze on some lemon juice.

Ink, ballpoint and felt tip: Dab stain with methylated spirits, and then wash. For washable ink,

soak in milk before laundering.

Mildew: Bleach white fabrics, or soak, then wash in heavy-duty detergent (with bleach).

Nail varnish: Mop up liquid, then with stain side facing down on kitchen paper, flush with nail polish remover (this is quite strong, and should not be used on some man-made fabrics – be sure to test first). Use methylated spirits (see box) to remove remaining nail-varnish colour.

Rust: Cover with salt, squeeze lemon juice over the salt and leave for about 1 hour; wash.

Safety note

Some of the cleaning agents you will need contain chemicals that are poisonous or flammable, so always read the label carefully and store them away from children. For safety, work in a well-ventilated area.

Websites

diynot.com

persil.co.uk

stainexpert.co.uk

recipediary.co.uk

Washing instructions

Nearly all fabrics are machine washable these days, and most washing machines handle them with care. Sort clothes and linens by colour and fabric type, and check labels.

Unless absolutely necessary, try to wash clothes at 30 degrees, as this uses less energy and is kinder to the environment. In any case, avoid washing an item at a higher temperature than recommended by the manufacturer, because this can cause it to shrink or change colour.

Every so often, run a higher temperature programme with the machine empty, to clean out greasy residues and kill off any bacteria.

Loading tips

■ Fill your washing machine loosely. Overloading not only adds to the number of creases that will need ironing out, but can damage your clothes and even your machine.

■ If you are washing woollens, this may mean washing just two or three items in one load.

Textile cycles

Check both the temperature, given by the figure in the tub, and the machine-action bar(s) under it. The temperature may be indicated by dots (six for 95°, four for 60°, two for 40° and one for 30°).

 Maximum agitation. Cotton cycle
White cotton or linen articles without special finishes.

 Maximum agitation. Cotton cycle
Cotton, linen or viscose articles without special finishes where colours are fast at 60°C.

 Maximum agitation. Cotton cycle
Cotton, linen or viscose where colours are fast at 40°C but not at 60°C.

 Medium agitation. Synthetic cycle
Acrylics, acetate or triacetate, including mixtures with wool, polyester and wool blends.

 Minimum agitation. Wool cycle
Wool, including blankets, wool mixed with other fibres, and silk.

 Gentle agitation. Delicates cycle
Silk, acetates and mixed synthetics not colourfast at 40°C.

 Hand wash only
See garment label for further instructions.

 Do not machine or hand wash

Washing process

Garments with labels showing the wash tub without the bar may be mixed with those that do, provided that they are washed at the lowest temperature shown and the gentlest setting of machine agitation to protect delicate items.

No bar
Normal – maximum machine action

1 bar
Medium – reduced machine action

2 bars
Minimum – lowest machine action

Washing symbols

Wash tub: Washing process

Triangle: Bleaching

iron: Ironing settings

Square: Drying methods

Circle: Dry cleaning

Dry-cleaning/bleaching

A circle shows the item may be dry-cleaned and the letter P or F indicates the cleaning fluids that may be used by your professional dry-cleaner.

May be dry-cleaned

Do not dry-clean

Bleach may be used

Do not use chlorine bleach

Do not bleach

Drying symbols

Check the label to see if garment can be tumble-dried; the label may advise using a reduced heat setting by putting a single dot within the circle. Two dots indicate a higher heat setting.

May be tumble-dried

Do not tumble-dry

Hang dry

Drip dry recommended

Dry flat

Ironing

■ The dots inside the iron indicate the temperature setting. One dot represents the coolest setting and three dots the hottest. The table (right) is a guide to the temperature to use for specific types of fabric.

■ You should always use the setting recommended by the manufacturer. For some materials the advice may be that you iron on the wrong side of the fabric only, so check the label.

■ To avoid creases, store your clothes in drawers and wardrobes loosely; don't pack them in.

Hot (3 dots)
Cotton, linen and viscose fabrics.

Warm (2 dots)
Polyester mixtures and wool.

Cool (1 dot)   Acrylic, nylon, acetate, triacetate and polyester.

Do not iron

First aid kit

Be prepared! Ensure you have the right kit, should an accident or emergency occur. Your first aid kit should be locked and kept in a cool, dry place, out of reach of children.

- Medicines should be checked regularly to make sure they are within their use-by dates.
- It is also useful to keep a small first aid kit ready to hand in the car.
- Purchase a bag or container with good handles that will hold your first aid items.

Check list

☐ Plasters, in a variety of different sizes and shapes	☐ Sticky tape
☐ Small, medium and large sterile gauze dressings	☐ Digital thermometer
☐ Two sterile eye dressings	☐ Skin rash cream, such as hydrocortisone or calendula
☐ Triangular bandages	☐ Cream or spray to relieve insect bites and stings
☐ Crêpe rolled bandages	☐ Antiseptic cream
☐ Safety pins	☐ Painkillers such as paracetamol or ibuprofen
☐ Disposable sterile gloves	☐ Child-friendly painkillers (if applicable)
☐ Tweezers	☐ Antihistamine tablets
☐ Scissors	☐ Distilled water, for cleaning wounds
☐ Alcohol-free cleansing wipes	☐ Eye wash and eye bath

2017
DIARY

December

M	T	W	T	F	S	S	M	T	W	T	F	S	S	M	T
26	27	28	29	30	31	1	2	3	4	5	6	7	8	9	10

26 Monday

Boxing Day
Bank Holiday, UK

Meal ideas

27 Tuesday

Bank Holiday, UK

Meal ideas

28 Wednesday

Meal ideas

29 Thursday

● New Moon

Meal ideas

30 Friday

Meal ideas

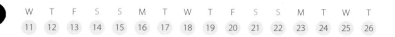

Saturday **31**
New Year's Eve

Meal ideas

January Sunday **1**
New Year's Day

Meal ideas

Mocha Cocktail

V

Coffee granules 1 tsp
Irish cream liqueur 60ml (2fl oz)
Chocolate flavoured milk 225ml
(8fl oz)
Vanilla ice cream 3 scoops
Grated chocolate to serve (optional)

Time 5 mins   Serves 3
Calories 206 per portion
Fat 7g of which 3.9g is saturated

1 Dissolve coffee granules in 1
tablespoon hot water and stir into
Irish cream liqueur.
2 Pour coffee and liqueur into a
blender. Add chocolate milk and ice
cream and blend until smooth.
3 Pour into three glasses, sprinkle
with grated chocolate and serve.

37

January
Week 1

2 Monday
Bank holiday, UK

Meal ideas

3 Tuesday
Bank holiday, Scotland

Meal ideas

4 Wednesday

Meal ideas

5 Thursday
❭ First Quarter

Meal ideas

6 Friday
Epiphany

Meal ideas

Saturday 7

Meal ideas

Sunday 8

Meal ideas

Cranberry Cheesecake ❄

Butter 50g (2oz), melted
Digestive biscuits 150g (5oz), crushed
Powdered gelatine 1 sachet
Full fat soft cheese 200g (7oz)
Caster sugar 50g (2oz)
Natural yogurt 150g (5oz)
Orange 1 small, finely grated zest and juice
Double cream 150ml (¼ pint)
Cranberry sauce 200g (7oz)

1 Mix butter and biscuit crumbs together.
Press into base of a 20cm (8in) loose-
bottomed cake tin. Chill.
2 Sprinkle gelatine over 3 tbsp cold water in a
cup, leave to soak for 5 minutes. Stand cup in a
pan of simmering water and stir until gelatine
has dissolved.
3 Mix soft cheese and sugar together in a
bowl then stir in yogurt and orange zest. Whip
cream until it forms soft swirls then fold into
cheese mixture. Gradually fold in orange juice.
4 In a separate bowl mix cranberry sauce with
1 tablespoon of dissolved gelatine. Gradually
fold the remainder into cheesecake mixture.
5 Pour half cheesecake into tin. Dot half
cranberry mix on top. Cover with remaining
cheesecake, dot remaining cranberry mix
on top and swirl together to give a marbled
effect. Chill for 4 hours or overnight until set.
6 Loosen edge of cheesecake, remove the tin
and transfer to a serving plate.

Time 15 mins   Serves 6
Calories 498 per portion
Fat 34g of which 19.1g is saturated

39

9 Monday

Meal ideas

10 Tuesday

Meal ideas

11 Wednesday

Meal ideas

12 Thursday
○ Full Moon

Meal ideas

13 Friday

Meal ideas

W	T	F	S	S	M	T	W	T	F	S	S	M	T	W	T
25	26	27	28	29	30	31	1	2	3	4	5	6	7	8	9

January
Week 2

Saturday 14

Meal ideas

Sunday 15

Meal ideas

Cauliflower Crisp

V

Cauliflower 1, broken into florets
Tomato 1, cut into wedges
Butter 40g (1½oz)
Mushrooms 225g (8oz), wiped and sliced
Plain flour 25g (1oz)
Milk 300ml (½ pint)
Cheddar cheese 175g (6oz), grated
Fresh breadcrumbs 2 tbsp

1 Steam cauliflower for 10 minutes or until tender. Drain and place in a shallow ovenproof dish with tomato.
2 Heat butter in a pan and gently fry mushrooms for 3 minutes. Add flour and milk to pan and bring up to boil, stirring. Cook for 2 minutes. Remove from heat and stir in 110g (4oz) cheese. Season to taste. Pour sauce over cauliflower and tomato.
3 Combine remaining cheese with breadcrumbs and sprinkle over cauliflower. Brown under a hot grill.

Time 20 mins   Serves 4
Calories 396 per portion
Fat 27g of which 15.6g is saturated

January
Week 3

M	T	W	T	F	S	S	M	T	W	T	F	S	S	M	T
16	**17**	**18**	**19**	**20**	**21**	**22**	23	24	25	26	27	28	29	30	31

16 Monday

Meal ideas

17 Tuesday

Meal ideas

18 Wednesday

Meal ideas

19 Thursday
☾ Last Quarter

Meal ideas

20 Friday

Meal ideas

Saturday 21

Meal ideas

Sunday 22

Meal ideas

Sausage Meatballs on Linguini

Olive oil 3 tbsp
Onion 1 large, finely chopped
Dried mixed herbs 2 tsp
Pork sausage meat 450g (1lb)
Chopped tomatoes 400g can
Chicken stock cube 1, crumbled
Linguini 350g (12oz)
Parmesan shavings to serve (optional)
Chopped parsley to serve (optional)

Time 40 mins   Serves 4
Calories 614 per portion
Fat 38g of which 10.6g is saturated

1 Heat 1 tbsp of oil in a non-stick frying pan, add onion and cook over a moderate heat until softened, but not browned. Transfer to a mixing bowl and leave to cool.
2 Add herbs and sausage meat to onion, season and mix well. Roll mixture into a log, cut into 12 and then roll each piece into a ball.
3 Pour tomatoes into a saucepan, add stock cube and bring up to boil. Reduce heat and leave to simmer gently.
4 Meanwhile, heat remaining oil in frying pan. Add meatballs and cook for 6–8 minutes, turning frequently, until lightly browned and cooked through.
5 Cook linguini according to packet's instructions and drain well. Serve in warmed pasta bowls topped with tomato sauce, meatballs, Parmesan shavings and chopped parsley, plus a generous sprinkling of coarsely ground black pepper if you like.

23 Monday

Meal ideas

24 Tuesday

Meal ideas

25 Wednesday

Burns' Night

Meal ideas

26 Thursday

Meal ideas

27 Friday

Meal ideas

Saturday **28**
● New Moon

Meal ideas

Sunday **29**

Meal ideas

Sizzling Beef with Noodles

Worcester sauce 1 tbsp
Soy sauce 2 tbsp
Tomato purée 1 tbsp
Sherry vinegar 1 tbsp
Honey 1 tbsp
Sesame oil 2 tsp
Sunflower oil 2 tsp
Rump steak 650g (1lb 7oz), trimmed and sliced
Sesame seeds 2 tbsp
Bamboo shoots 225g can, drained
Baby corn 175g (6oz), halved
Microwave rice noodles 300g packet

1 Mix together sauces, tomato purée, vinegar and honey. Leave to stand for 10 minutes.
2 Heat oils in a wok or large frying pan and stir-fry steak on a high heat for 1 minute.
3 Add sesame seeds, sauce, bamboo shoots and corn and cook for 3 minutes, stirring.
4 Heat noodles according to packet's instructions, drain and serve with beef and vegetables.

Time 10 mins plus standing Serves 4
Calories 483 per portion
Fat 25g of which 7g is saturated

January
Week 5

M	T	W	T	F	S	S	M	T	W	T	F	S	S	M	T
30	**31**	**1**	**2**	**3**	**4**	**5**	6	7	8	9	10	11	12	13	14

30 Monday

Meal ideas

31 Tuesday

Meal ideas

1 Wednesday February

Meal ideas

2 Thursday

Meal ideas

3 Friday

Meal ideas

W	T	F	S	S	M	T	W	T	F	S	S	M	T	W	T
15	16	17	18	19	20	21	22	23	24	25	26	27	28	1	2

February
Week 5

Saturday 4
❯ First Quarter

Meal ideas

Sunday 5

Meal ideas

Fruity Marmalade

V

Seville oranges 1.35kg (3lb), halved
Lemons 3 large, halved
Pineapple 680g (1½lb), thickly sliced and cut into 8mm (⅜in) pieces
Preserving sugar 2.7kg (6lb)

Time 2½–3 hrs   Makes 3.5kg (7-8lb)
Calories 81 per portion
Fat 0g of which 0g is saturated

1 Squeeze and strain juice from oranges and lemons. Pull away membrane, taking care not to remove the white pith, and discard.
2 Cut orange and lemon caps into thick or fine shreds and put into a large non-reactive preserving pan.
3 Add 2.5 litres (4 pints) water and bring to the boil, then reduce heat and cook gently for about 1½ hours, until peel is softened, but not broken up.
4 Add pineapple and sugar, stir until dissolved, and then bring to the boil and boil gently for about 45 minutes until setting point is reached. To test for a set, spoon some marmalade onto a saucer, leave until cold and gently push finger through it – if it wrinkles well, marmalade is ready. If not, repeat at 10 minute intervals.
5 Allow to settle for 5 minutes, then pour into warmed jars and cover with waxed paper discs. Add cellophane covers when cold and store in a cool place.

47

6 Monday

Accession of Queen Elizabeth II

Meal ideas

7 Tuesday

Meal ideas

8 Wednesday

Meal ideas

9 Thursday

Meal ideas

10 Friday

Meal ideas

Saturday 11
○ Full Moon

Meal ideas

Sunday 12
Septuagesima Sunday

Meal ideas

Venison & Cranberry Casserole ❄

Rindless smoked back bacon 250g (9oz), chopped
Venison suitable for casserole (or beef) 1.2kg (2lb 10oz), diced
Plain flour 2 tbsp, seasoned with salt and pepper
Sunflower oil 2-3 tbsp
Shallots 16, peeled
Garlic 2 cloves, peeled and crushed
Ground mixed spice 1 tsp
Red wine 75cl bottle
Fresh (or frozen) cranberries 300g (11oz)
Soft light brown sugar 1 tbsp
Beef gravy 300ml (½ pint)

Time 2-2½ hrs   Serves 6
Calories 438 per portion
Fat 15g of which 4.7g is saturated

1 In a flameproof casserole or pan cook bacon in its own fat until crisp. Set aside.
2 Coat venison in flour. Add half the oil to the casserole and cook venison in batches until browned on all sides, adding more oil as necessary. Set aside.
3 Add shallots and garlic and cook for 5 minutes until starting to brown, stirring occasionally.
4 Return venison and bacon to casserole, stir in spice and wine and slowly bring to the boil. Reduce heat and simmer gently for 1-1½ hours or until meat is tender.
5 Stir in cranberries, sugar and gravy and season to taste. Partially cover and simmer for a further 30 minutes or until cranberries have softened.

February

Week 7

13 Monday

Meal ideas

14 Tuesday

St Valentine's Day

Meal ideas

15 Wednesday

Meal ideas

16 Thursday

Meal ideas

17 Friday

Meal ideas

Saturday 18
☾ Last Quarter

Meal ideas

Sunday 19

Meal ideas

Champagne Cocktail

V

Strawberries 150g (5oz), hulled
Caster sugar 15g (½oz)
Gin 2 tbsp, chilled
Champagne or sparkling white wine
350–400ml (12–14fl oz), chilled
Strawberries 2 large, halved
lengthways, to serve

1 In advance of serving (which can
be several hours), roughly chop
strawberries, place in a small bowl
with caster sugar and mix together.
Cover and leave for at least 20
minutes, or until the sugar has
dissolved and strawberries are soft.
2 Spoon strawberries into a nylon
sieve over a bowl and crush
with a spoon to extract all juice.
Strain though sieve into a jug and
refrigerate. Discard pulp.
3 When ready to serve, pour
strawberry juice into two chilled
glasses and add 1 tbsp of gin to each.
Pour in champagne, stir, add halved
strawberry and serve immediately.

Time 25 mins   Serves 2
Calories 211 per portion
Fat 0g of which 0g is saturated

51

February
Week 8

20 Monday

Meal ideas

21 Tuesday

Meal ideas

22 Wednesday

Meal ideas

23 Thursday

Meal ideas

24 Friday

Meal ideas

W	T	F	S	S	M	T	W	T	F	S	S	M	T	W	T
8	9	10	11	12	13	14	15	16	17	18	19	20	21	22	23

February
Week 8

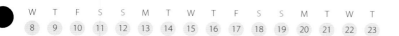

Saturday 25

Meal ideas

Sunday 26
● New Moon

Quinquagesima Sunday

Meal ideas

Cauliflower & Potato Curry **V** ❄

Olive oil 1 tbsp
Onion 1, peeled and sliced
Garlic 1 clove, peeled and crushed
Potatoes 500g (1lb 2oz), peeled and cut into chunks
Vegetable stock 1.2 litres (2 pints)
Fine green beans 110g (4oz), trimmed and sliced
Cauliflower ½, broken into florets
Baby corn 175g (6oz), halved
Curry paste 3 tbsp
Pilau rice and naan bread to serve (optional)

Time 30 mins   Serves 4
Calories 224 per portion
Fat 7g of which 0.8g is saturated

1 Heat oil in a pan and sauté onion for 4 minutes, until softened. Add garlic and cook for a further minute.
2 Add potatoes and stock, bring to the boil, then simmer for 10 minutes, covered. Add vegetables and cook for 10 minutes more.
3 Stir in curry paste and cook for 2 minutes. Serve with pilau rice and warmed naan, if using.

M T W T F S S M T W T F S S M T
27 **28** **1** **2** **3** **4** **5** 6 7 8 9 10 11 12 13 14

27 Monday

Meal ideas

28 Tuesday
Shrove Tuesday

Meal ideas

1 Wednesday March
St David's Day
Ash Wednesday

Meal ideas

2 Thursday

Meal ideas

3 Friday

Meal ideas

W	T	F	S	S	M	T	W	T	F	S	S	M	T	W	T
15	16	17	18	19	20	21	22	23	24	25	26	27	28	29	30

March
Week 9

Saturday 4

Meal ideas

Sunday 5
❭ First Quarter
Quagragesima Sunday

Meal ideas

Seafood Pancakes

Plain flour 150g (5oz)
Egg 1
Milk 750ml (1¼ pints)
Butter 25g (1oz), plus extra for frying
White fish fillet 350g (12oz), cut into 2.5cm (1in) cubes
Frozen peas 75g (3oz)
Seafood sticks 110g (4oz), chopped
Wholegrain mustard 2 tsp
Double Gloucester cheese with garlic and chives 50g (2oz), grated

1 Place 110g (4oz) flour in a bowl, break in egg. Gradually add 300ml (½ pint) milk, beating to make a smooth batter.
2 Heat a sliver of butter in a non-stick frying pan. Add 3 tbsp batter and tilt to cover base. Cook until pancake moves freely, turn over and cook until golden. Repeat to make 8 pancakes and keep warm.
3 Place remaining flour, milk, 25g (1oz) butter in a pan and heat, stirring, until sauce thickens. Add fish and peas and cook for 5 minutes, add seafood sticks and warm through.
4 Remove from heat, add mustard and cheese and stir. Divide between pancakes and fold into triangles.

Time 30 mins   Serves 4
Calories 532 per portion
Fat 26g of which 15g is saturated

55

March
Week 10

M	T	W	T	F	S	S	M	T	W	T	F	S	S	M	T
6	7	8	9	10	11	12	13	14	15	16	17	18	19	20	21

6 Monday

Meal ideas

7 Tuesday

Meal ideas

8 Wednesday

Meal ideas

9 Thursday

Meal ideas

10 Friday

Meal ideas

W	T	F	S	S	M	T	W	T	F	S	S	M	T	W	T
22	23	24	25	26	27	28	29	30	31	1	2	3	4	5	6

March
Week 10

Saturday 11

Meal ideas

Sunday 12
○ Full Moon

Meal ideas

Crunchy Peanut Brittle   V

Caster sugar 175g (6oz)
Golden syrup 75g (3oz)
Unsalted peanuts 175g (6oz)
Unsalted butter 15g (½ oz)

Time 20 mins plus cooling
Makes 425g (15oz)
Calories 72 per 15g (½oz)
Fat 3g of which 0.8g is saturated

1 Place caster sugar and syrup in a heavy-based saucepan and add 125ml (4fl oz) cold water. Fill a jug with boiling water.
2 Heat gently, stirring continuously, until sugar is completely dissolved, brushing sides of pan with hot water occasionally.
3 Add peanuts to sugar syrup and bring up to boil. Boil, without stirring, for 7-10 minutes until mixture turns to a rich golden caramel colour.
4 Immediately remove from heat and add butter. Mix into caramel by tilting pan – do not stir. Quickly pour onto an oiled baked sheet. Leave to cool and set hard.
5 When cold, break into pieces and store in a tin, interleaved with non-stick baking paper.

57

March
Week 11

M	T	W	T	F	S	S	M	T	W	T	F	S	S	M	T
13	14	15	16	17	18	19	20	21	22	23	24	25	26	27	28

13 Monday

Meal ideas

14 Tuesday

Meal ideas

15 Wednesday

Meal ideas

16 Thursday

Meal ideas

17 Friday

St Patrick's Day
Bank holiday, N Ireland

Meal ideas

W	T	F	S	S	M	T	W	T	F	S	S	M	T	W	T
29	30	31	1	2	3	4	5	6	7	8	9	10	11	12	13

March
Week 11

Saturday **18**

Meal ideas

Sunday **19**

Meal ideas

Irish Soda Bread with Rosemary

V ❄

Plain flour 450g (1lb)
Irish porridge oats with multi seeds
50g (2oz)
Salt 1 tsp
Bicarbonate of soda 1 tsp
Butter or white fat 25g (1oz), chopped
Finely chopped fresh rosemary
2 tbsp
Fresh cultured buttermilk 300ml pot
Whole milk 100ml (3½fl oz)

Time 45 mins   Makes 1 loaf
Calories 140 per slice
Fat 2g of which 1.2g is saturated

1 Preheat oven to 200ºC/180ºfan/Gas
6. Mix together flour, oats, salt and
bicarbonate of soda. Add butter or
fat and rub in until it resembles fine
breadcrumbs. Stir in rosemary.
2 Add buttermilk and enough milk
to make a soft but not sticky dough.
Transfer to a greased and floured
baking sheet and shape into an 18cm
(7in) round. With a knife, score into
four and bake for 30-40 minutes or
until golden and cooked through.
3 Serve bread warm with soup or a
selection of cheeses and pickles.

Cook's tip If you can't find oats with
seeds, use plain Irish porridge oats
instead.

M T W T F S S M T W T F S S M T
20 **21** **22** **23** **24** **25** **26** 27 28 29 30 31 1 2 3 4

20 Monday
☾ Last Quarter

Vernal equinox

Spring begins

Meal ideas

21 Tuesday

Meal ideas

22 Wednesday

Meal ideas

23 Thursday

Meal ideas

24 Friday

Meal ideas

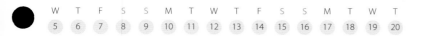
Saturday 25

Don't forget to put your clocks forward 1 hour tonight

Meal ideas

Sunday 26

British Summer Time begins

Mothering Sunday

Fourth Sunday in Lent

Meal ideas

Oaty Fudge Treats

V ❄

Milk 150ml (¼ pint)
Brown sugar 450g (1lb)
Butter 15g (½oz)
Salt pinch
Vanilla essence ½ tsp
Crunchy peanut butter 175g (6oz)
Porridge oats 110g (4oz)
No added sugar muesli 110g (4oz)
Glacè cherries 75g (3oz), chopped

1 Place milk, sugar, butter, salt and vanilla essence in a pan and bring to the boil, stirring. Boil for 2 minutes, stirring, until the sugar has dissolved. Remove from heat.
2 Add peanut butter and stir, then add all remaining ingredients and mix well. Place spoonfuls of mixture into petit four cases and leave to set.

Time 10 mins   Makes 26
Calories 110 per portion
Fat 3g of which 0.9g is saturated

61

March

Week 13

27 Monday

Meal ideas

28 Tuesday

● New Moon

Meal ideas

29 Wednesday

Meal ideas

30 Thursday

Meal ideas

31 Friday

Meal ideas

W	T	F	S	S	M	T	W	T	F	S	S	M	T	W	T
12	13	14	15	16	17	18	19	20	21	22	23	24	25	26	27

April
Week 13

April **Saturday 1**

Meal ideas

Sunday 2

Meal ideas

Bacon & Brie Stuffed Croissants

Rindless unsmoked back bacon
6 rashers, cut into thin strips
Bake it Fresh croissant dough
250g can
Brie 110g (4oz), cut into 6 slices
Egg 1, beaten

1 Preheat oven to 200°C/ 180°fan/
Gas 6. Line a baking sheet with
greaseproof paper.
2 Heat a non-stick frying pan over
a medium heat and cook bacon for
8-10 minutes until crisp, adding a
little oil if necessary. Leave to cool.
3 Meanwhile, unroll croissant dough
and separate into triangles as
instructed on the can.
4 Place a slice of brie just in from the
base of each triangle, followed by a
few strips of bacon.
5 Roll croissants up from the base
of the triangle and transfer onto the
baking sheet, leaving about 5cm (2in)
between each. Brush with a little egg
to glaze and bake in oven for 10-15
minutes until golden.

Time 30 mins   Makes 6
Calories 245 per portion
Fat 15g of which 8.2g is saturated

63

3 Monday
❯ First Quarter

Meal ideas

4 Tuesday

Meal ideas

5 Wednesday

Meal ideas

6 Thursday

Meal ideas

7 Friday

Meal ideas

W	T	F	S	S	M	T	W	T	F	S	S	M	T	W	T
19	20	21	22	23	24	25	26	27	28	29	30	1	2	3	4

April
Week 14

Saturday 8

Meal ideas

Sunday 9
Palm Sunday

Meal ideas

Greek Spiced Lamb

Lean leg of lamb 750g (1lb 10oz), trimmed weight, cubed
Plain flour 3 tbsp
Mild or medium curry powder 2 tbsp
Natural Greek yogurt 250g (9oz)
Dried oregano 1 tbsp
Sun-dried tomato paste or tomato purée 2–3 tbsp
New potatoes to serve (optional)
Lemon vinaigrette to serve (optional
Coriander to garnish (optional)

1 Put lamb in a large bowl. Add flour and spice and toss until lamb is evenly coated. Add remaining ingredients and mix well.
2 Heat oven to 220°C/200°fan/Gas 7. Spread lamb in roasting tin and bake for 15 minutes. Reduce heat to 190°C/170°fan/Gas 5 and bake for another 25 minutes, turning occasionally, until cooked. If lamb starts to over-brown, cover with foil.
3 Serve with steamed new potatoes, tossed in chopped coriander and a lemon vinaigrette dressing, and garnish with coriander sprigs, if using.

Time 1 hr Serves 4
Calories 440 per portion
Fat 24g of which 11g is saturated

65

10 Monday

Meal ideas

11 Tuesday
○ Full Moon

Meal ideas

12 Wednesday

Meal ideas

13 Thursday

Meal ideas

14 Friday
Good Friday

Bank Holiday, UK

Meal ideas

W	T	F	S	S	M	T	W	T	F	S	S	M	T	W	T
26	27	28	29	30	1	2	3	4	5	6	7	8	9	10	11

April
Week 15

Saturday **15**

Meal ideas

Sunday **16**
Easter Day

Meal ideas

Simple Roast Lamb with Spring Veg

Half leg of lamb weighing about 1.8kg (4lb)
Garlic 4 cloves, peeled and crushed
Fresh rosemary 4 sprigs, leaves plucked and chopped
Olive oil 6 tbsp
Small new potatoes 750g (1lb 10oz), scrubbed
Chantenay carrots 500g (1lb 2oz), trimmed and scrubbed
Asparagus 2 bundles weighing about 500g (1lb 2oz), trimmed

Time 2½–3 hrs plus resting   Serves 6
Calories 625 per portion
Fat 34g of which 13g is saturated

1 Preheat oven to 190ºC/170ºfan/Gas 5. Place lamb in a roasting tin. Mix together garlic, rosemary and 2 tablespoons of olive oil with freshly ground black pepper. Spread all over lamb. Roast for 2–2½ hours, depending on how you like your meat cooked.
2 When lamb has an hour left to cook, bring potatoes (cut any big ones in half) and carrots to the boil in pan of water and simmer for 5 minutes. Meanwhile, put remaining oil in a roasting tin in the oven above lamb to heat up. Drain vegetables, add to hot oil and roast for 30 minutes. Remove from oven and add asparagus. Stir well and cook for a further 15 minutes or until vegetables are tender.
3 Leave lamb to rest for 10 minutes before carving. Serve with gravy made from juices left in pan.

April
Week 16

M	T	W	T	F	S	S	M	T	W	T	F	S	S	M	T
17	18	19	20	21	22	23	24	25	26	27	28	29	30	1	2

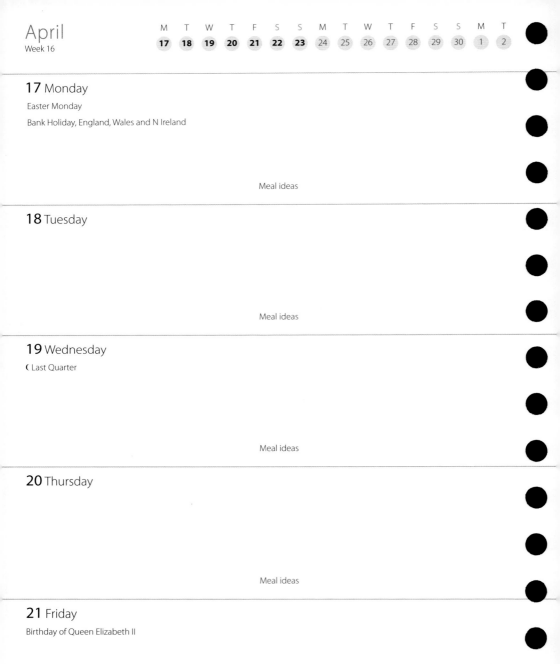

17 Monday

Easter Monday

Bank Holiday, England, Wales and N Ireland

Meal ideas

18 Tuesday

Meal ideas

19 Wednesday

(Last Quarter

Meal ideas

20 Thursday

Meal ideas

21 Friday

Birthday of Queen Elizabeth II

Meal ideas

Saturday 22

Meal ideas

Sunday 23

St George's Day

Low Sunday

Meal ideas

St George's Steak & Ale Pies

❄

Olive oil 3 tbsp
Onion 1, peeled and chopped
Rindless unsmoked back bacon
4 rashers, chopped
Carrots 2, peeled and sliced
Braising steak 700g (1½lb)
Flour 2 tbsp
Pale ale 1 x 500ml bottle
Beef stock 300ml (½ pint)
Dried mixed herbs ½ tsp
Puff pastry 500g
Egg 1, beaten

Time 3 hours   Serves 4
Calories 961 per portion
Fat 61g of which 25g is saturated

1 Heat half the oil in a large pan and cook onion for 5 minutes. Add bacon and cook for 3 minutes. Add carrots and cook for 3 minutes. Set aside.
2 Toss beef in flour and brown in remaining oil. Return onion mix to pan and mix well, then pour in ale and stock. Add herbs and bring to the boil, stirring. Cover and cook gently for 2 hours or until tender, stirring occasionally.
3 Divide meat between four individual pie dishes. Cool.
4 Preheat oven to 200°C/180°fan/Gas 6. Divide pastry into four. Roll each out 4cm (1½in) bigger than dish. For each pie: cut a strip of pastry for rim and attach with water. Press pastry onto dish. Trim excess and knock back edges. Glaze with egg and make a small hole. Set on a tray and bake for 30-40 minutes.

69

April
Week 17

M	T	W	T	F	S	S	M	T	W	T	F	S	S	M	T
24	**25**	**26**	**27**	**28**	**29**	**30**	1	2	3	4	5	6	7	8	9

24 Monday

Meal ideas

25 Tuesday

Meal ideas

26 Wednesday

● New Moon

Meal ideas

27 Thursday

Meal ideas

28 Friday

Meal ideas

Saturday **29**

Meal ideas

Sunday **30**

Meal ideas

Tangy Carrot Soup

❄

Onion 1, peeled and chopped
Carrots 450g (1lb), peeled and sliced
Bay leaf 1
Milk 300ml (½ pint)
Chicken stock 300ml (½ pint)
Orange 1, finely grated rind and juice
Single cream 150ml (¼ pint)
Croutons to serve (optional)

1 Put onion, carrots, bay leaf, milk and stock into a pan and bring up to boil. Simmer for about 20 minutes until carrots are tender.
2 Remove bay leaf, season to taste and purée until smooth. Add juice and most of the orange rind and heat gently until hot. Serve with a swirl of cream, sprinkle with remaining orange rind and croutons, if using.

Time 35 mins   Serves 4
Calories 168 per portion
Fat 9g of which 5.3g is saturated

71

M T W T F S S M T W T F S S M T
1 **2** **3** **4** **5** **6** **7** 8 9 10 11 12 13 14 15 16

1 Monday May
Bank Holiday, UK

Meal ideas

2 Tuesday

Meal ideas

3 Wednesday
❭ First Quarter

Meal ideas

4 Thursday

Meal ideas

5 Friday

Meal ideas

Saturday 6

Meal ideas

Sunday 7

Meal ideas

Easy Yogurt Cake

V ❄

Cherry yogurt 150g (5oz) tub
Self-raising flour 175g (6oz), sifted
Caster sugar 150g (5oz)
Butter 25g (1oz), melted
Eggs 2 medium, beaten
Chopped mixed peel 50g (2oz)
Flaked almonds 15g (½oz)

1 Preheat oven to 180°C/160°fan/
Gas 4. Grease and line a 900g (2lb)
loaf tin.
2 In a large bowl, mix together
yogurt, flour, sugar, butter and eggs
until smooth. Add mixed peel, stir
and then pour into prepared tin.
3 Sprinkle almonds along the centre
of the mixture then bake in the oven
for 30-35 minutes until a skewer
comes out clean. Cool in tin for 15
minutes before turning out.

Time 40 mins   Makes 10 slices
Calories 188 per portion
Fat 5g of which 2g is saturated

73

M T W T F S S M T W T F S S M T
8 **9** **10** **11** **12** **13** **14** 15 16 17 18 19 20 21 22 23

8 Monday

Meal ideas

9 Tuesday

Meal ideas

10 Wednesday
○ Full Moon

Meal ideas

11 Thursday

Meal ideas

12 Friday

Meal ideas

W	T	F	S	S	M	T	W	T	F	S	S	M	T	W	T
24	25	26	27	28	29	30	31	1	2	3	4	5	6	7	8

May
Week 19

Saturday 13

Meal ideas

Sunday 14

Meal ideas

Walnut & Parsley Pesto Chicken

Walnuts 15g (½oz), roughly chopped
Garlic 1 clove, peeled and crushed
Salt ½ tsp
Flat-leaf parsley 50g (2oz), leaves only
Grated Parmesan cheese 3 tbsp
Olive oil 6 tbsp
Skinless chicken breasts 4, cut into thin strips
Crème fraîche 4 tbsp
Tagliatelle to serve (optional)

Time 20 mins   Serves 4
Calories 409 per portion
Fat 29g of which 8.1g is saturated

1 Dry-fry walnuts in a non-stick frying pan until lightly toasted.
2 Put walnuts, garlic, salt and parsley into a food processor and pulse to a rough texture. Add Parmesan cheese and 5 tbsp oil. Whizz to blend, but still leave slightly chunky.
3 Heat remaining oil in a wok or frying pan and add chicken strips. Cook for 4–5 minutes until browned.
4 Add crème fraîche and 3 tbsp of parsley pesto and simmer for 5 minutes.
5 Mix in 2 tbsp extra pesto and serve with tagliatelle, if using.

Cook's tip Put leftover pesto in a bowl alongside for extra drizzling.

M	T	W	T	F	S	S	M	T	W	T	F	S	S	M	T
15	**16**	**17**	**18**	**19**	**20**	**21**	22	23	24	25	26	27	28	29	30

15 Monday

Meal ideas

16 Tuesday

Meal ideas

17 Wednesday

Meal ideas

18 Thursday

Meal ideas

19 Friday
☾ Last Quarter

Meal ideas

W	T	F	S	S	M	T	W	T	F	S	S	M	T	W	T
31	1	2	3	4	5	6	7	8	9	10	11	12	13	14	15

May
Week 20

Saturday 20

Meal ideas

Sunday 21

Meal ideas

Chocolate Orange Charlotte ❄

Plain chocolate 175g (6oz), broken into chunks
Milk 300ml (½ pint)
Orange liqueur 2 tbsp
Eggs 2, separated
Soft light brown sugar 50g (2oz)
Powdered gelatine 15g (½oz), dissolved in 3 tbsp hot water
Oranges 2, finely grated rind and juice
Double cream 300ml (½ pint)
Sponge fingers about 15, halved
Grated chocolate and finely grated rind of 1 orange to decorate

Time 45 mins plus chilling   Serves 6-8
Calories 417 per portion
Fat 30g of which 16.4g is saturated

1 Gently heat chocolate in a small pan with milk until melted. Stir in orange liqueur.
2 Beat egg yolks and sugar together until creamy. Stir into chocolate.
3 Heat gently, stirring until thickened. Stir in gelatine, orange rind and juice. Cool.
4 Lightly whip and fold in 150ml (¼ pint) cream. Whisk egg whites until stiff and fold into mixture.
5 Pour into a lightly greased, loose-bottomed, 20cm (8in) deep cake tin and chill until set.
6 Turn out onto a plate, whip remaining cream, use a little to stick sponge fingers around sides of the chocolate then spread rest over the top. Decorate with chocolate and orange rind.

M	T	W	T	F	S	S	M	T	W	T	F	S	S	M	T
22	23	24	25	26	27	28	29	30	31	1	2	3	4	5	6

22 Monday

Meal ideas

23 Tuesday

Meal ideas

24 Wednesday

Meal ideas

25 Thursday
● New Moon

Ascension Day

Holy Thursday

Meal ideas

26 Friday

Meal ideas

Saturday **27**

Meal ideas

Sunday **28**

Meal ideas

Thai Turkey Noodles

Sesame oil 1 tbsp
Sunflower oil 1 tbsp
Turkey fillets 2, thinly sliced
Spring onions 6, trimmed and sliced
Garlic purée 1 tsp
Ginger purée 1 tsp
Lemon grass 2 blades, finely sliced
Chilli paste ½-1 tsp
Coconut cream 50g (2oz)
Straight-to-wok noodles 2 x 150g (5oz) packs
Soy sauce 2 tbsp
Beansprouts about 200g (7oz)

1 Heat oils in a wok or frying pan and stir-fry turkey for 3 minutes.
2 Add onions, garlic, ginger, lemon grass, chilli, coconut and 150ml (¼ pint) water. Stir-fry for 2 minutes then add noodles and soy sauce. Stir for 2 minutes.
3 Add beansprouts and cook for a further 2 minutes.

Time 15 mins Serves 4
Calories 319 per portion
Fat 12g of which 4.9g is saturated

79

May
Week 22

M	T	W	T	F	S	S	M	T	W	T	F	S	S	M	T
29	30	31	1	2	3	4	5	6	7	8	9	10	11	12	13

29 Monday
Bank Holiday, UK

Meal ideas

30 Tuesday

Meal ideas

31 Wednesday

Meal ideas

1 Thursday June
❯ First Quarter

Meal ideas

2 Friday
Coronation Day

Meal ideas

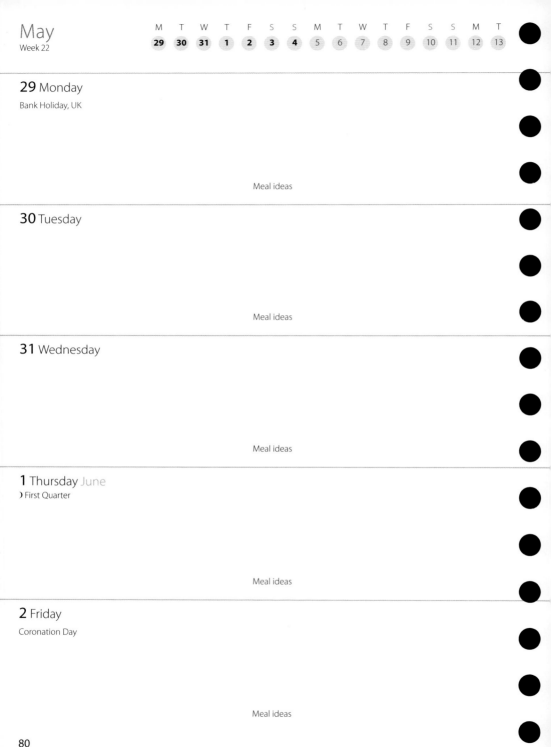

Saturday 3

Meal ideas

Sunday 4

Whit Sunday

Pentecost

Meal ideas

Candy Rice Pudding

V

Milk 600ml (1 pint)
Pudding rice 50g (2oz)
Caster sugar 2 tsp
Caramac candy bar 50g (2oz)

1 Place milk, rice and sugar in a pan. Bring to the boil, stirring. Cover and simmer for 30 minutes until rice is cooked, stirring occasionally.
2 Break up and stir in most of the candy bar. Serve hot or cold with the remaining candy on top to decorate.

Time 40 mins   Serves 4
Calories 179 per portion
Fat 6g of which 2.8g is saturated

June
Week 23

M	T	W	T	F	S	S	M	T	W	T	F	S	S	M	T
5	**6**	**7**	**8**	**9**	**10**	**11**	12	13	14	15	16	17	18	19	20

5 Monday

Meal ideas

6 Tuesday

Meal ideas

7 Wednesday

Meal ideas

8 Thursday

Meal ideas

9 Friday
❍ Full Moon

Meal ideas

W	T	F	S	S	M	T	W	T	F	S	S	M	T	W	T
21	22	23	24	25	26	27	28	29	30	1	2	3	4	5	6

June
Week 23

Saturday 10

Meal ideas

Sunday 11
Trinity Sunday

Meal ideas

Smoked Trout Pâté

Trout fillets 2 large, about 450g (1lb)
Aromatics: 1 large sprig **parsley**, thick slice of
lemon, bay leaf, 1 tsp **black peppercorns**
Smoked trout 125g packet, flaked
Crème fraîche 200g (7oz)
Lemon juice 2 tbsp
Butter 110g (4oz)
Black peppercorns 2 tbsp, coarsely crushed
Sprig of watercress to serve (optional)

Time 55 mins   Serves 4
Calories 550 per portion
Fat 48g of which 28.4g is saturated

1 Put trout into a large non-reactive pan. Cover
with cold water, add aromatics and bring up
to boil. Remove from heat, cover with a lid and
leave in a cool place until cold. Drain.
2 Flake the trout's flesh and put it into a
blender. Add smoked trout and blend briefly,
retaining some texture.
3 Transfer fish into a bowl, add crème fraîche
and lemon juice. Season to taste with salt and
spoon into a 600ml (1 pint) soufflé dish, or 6
individual containers, and smooth top.
4 Melt butter in a small pan and cool slightly.
Carefully pour clear yellow butter into a small
bowl, leaving the white milky liquid in the pan.
Discard milky liquid.
5 Stir peppercorns into butter, pour on top of
pâté and refrigerate until set. Cover and keep
refrigerated until serving – it will keep well for
4–5 days. Serve pâté with seeded or granary
bread or toast, or water biscuits. Garnish with
watercress, if using.

83

M T W T F S S M T W T F S S M T
12 13 14 15 16 17 18 19 20 21 22 23 24 25 26 27

12 Monday

Meal ideas

13 Tuesday

Meal ideas

14 Wednesday

Meal ideas

15 Thursday

Corpus Christi

Meal ideas

16 Friday

Meal ideas

W	T	F	S	S	M	T	W	T	F	S	S	M	T	W	T
28	29	30	1	2	3	4	5	6	7	8	9	10	11	12	13

June
Week 24

Saturday **17**
☾ Last Quarter

Meal ideas

Sunday **18**
Father's Day

Meal ideas

Teriyaki Beef Skewers

Lean beef steak 450g (1lb), cubed
Red peppers 2, deseeded and cut into slices
Garlic 1 clove, peeled and crushed
Root ginger 2.5cm (1in) piece, peeled and finely chopped
Soy sauce 2 tbsp
Dry sherry 1 tbsp
Clear honey 1 tbsp
Sesame oil 1 tsp
Pack of stir-fry vegetables to serve (optional)
Plain boiled rice to serve (optional)

Time 15 mins plus marinating
Serves 4
Calories 195 per portion
Fat 6g of which 2g is saturated

1 Soak 8 bamboo skewers in warm water until required.
2 Place all ingredients, except stir-fry vegetables and rice, in a bowl and mix together. Leave to marinate for 30 minutes.
3 Thread beef and red pepper slices onto each skewer. Reserve juices.
4 Grill skewers on medium heat for 3–4 minutes on each side, brushing with juices occasionally.
5 Strain remaining juices into a pan, bring to boil and simmer until syrupy. Serve kebabs on rice with vegetables, if using, and drizzled with syrup.

M T W T F S S M T W T F S S M T
19 **20** **21** **22** **23** **24** **25** 26 27 28 29 30 1 2 3 4

19 Monday

Meal ideas

20 Tuesday

Meal ideas

21 Wednesday

Summer solstice
Summer begins

Meal ideas

22 Thursday

Meal ideas

23 Friday

Meal ideas

Saturday **24**
● New Moon

Meal ideas

Sunday **25**

Meal ideas

New Potato & Bean Salad   V

Small new potatoes 500g (1lb 2oz), washed
Garlic 1 clove, unpeeled
Olive oil 4 tbsp
Runner beans 110g (4oz), sliced
French or green beans 110g (4oz), trimmed
Shelled broad beans 110g (4oz)
Cider vinegar 1 tbsp
Cherry tomatoes 10, halved
Capers 1 tbsp
Chopped chives 1 tbsp

1 Preheat oven to 200°C/180°fan/ Gas 6. Roast potatoes and garlic in 1 tbsp of oil for 35-40 minutes, shaking tin occasionally, until softened.
2 Meanwhile boil all beans for 3-4 minutes, until just tender. Drain and refresh under cold water.
3 Remove potatoes and garlic from the oven and squeeze garlic purée from its skin. Blend with the vinegar and remaining oil and season with salt and freshly ground black pepper.
4 In a bowl, mix beans with warm potatoes, tomatoes, capers and dressing. Sprinkle with chives.

Time 1 hr Serves 4
Calories 225 per portion
Fat 12g of which 1.6g is saturated

June
Week 26

M	T	W	T	F	S	S	M	T	W	T	F	S	S	M	T
26	**27**	**28**	**29**	**30**	**1**	**2**	3	4	5	6	7	8	9	10	11

26 Monday

Meal ideas

27 Tuesday

Meal ideas

28 Wednesday

Meal ideas

29 Thursday

Meal ideas

30 Friday

Meal ideas

July **Saturday 1**
☽ First Quarter

Meal ideas

Sunday 2

Meal ideas

Potato, Beetroot & Mackerel Salad

New potatoes 450g (1lb), scrubbed and halved
Olive oil 6 tbsp
Red wine vinegar 3 tbsp
Caster sugar 2 tsp
Grainy mustard 2 tsp
Sugarsnap peas 100g (3½oz), shredded
Spring onions ½ bunch, thinly sliced
Smoked peppered mackerel 250g (9oz), skinned and broken into chunks
Cooked beetroot 200g (7oz), cut into matchsticks

Time 25 mins   Serves 4
Calories 494 per portion
Fat 36g of which 7g is saturated

1 Cook new potatoes in simmering water for 10-15 minutes, until tender. Drain well.
2 Meanwhile, mix oil, vinegar, sugar and mustard together.
3 Put sugarsnap peas in a salad bowl with spring onions, mackerel and beetroot.
4 Add potatoes to the bowl with dressing and fold gently together.

3 Monday

Meal ideas

4 Tuesday

Meal ideas

5 Wednesday

Meal ideas

6 Thursday

Meal ideas

7 Friday

Meal ideas

Saturday **8**

Meal ideas

Sunday **9**
○ Full Moon

Meal ideas

Minty Lamb Burgers ❄

Onion 1, peeled and finely chopped
Lean minced lamb 350g (12oz)
Breadcrumbs 4 tbsp
Mint jelly 3 tbsp
Low fat natural fromage frais 4 tbsp
Apple sauce 4 tbsp
Chopped mint leaves 1 tbsp
Wholemeal baps 4
Salad leaves and cucumber to serve

1 Mix onion, lamb, breadcrumbs and 2 tablespoons mint jelly in a bowl. Divide into four equal portions and form into 10cm (4in) burgers. Chill for 30 minutes.
2 For the relish, mix together fromage frais, apple sauce, remaining mint jelly and chopped mint. Chill until required.
3 Cook burgers under a medium grill for 7–8 minutes on each side until cooked. Serve in baps with cucumber slices, salad leaves and apple mint relish.

Time 30 mins plus chilling   Serves 4
Calories 340 per portion
Fat 9g of which 3.8g is saturated

91

10 Monday

Meal ideas

11 Tuesday

Meal ideas

12 Wednesday

Bank Holiday, N Ireland

Meal ideas

13 Thursday

Meal ideas

14 Friday

Meal ideas

W	T	F	S	S	M	T	W	T	F	S	S	M	T	W	T
26	27	28	29	30	31	1	2	3	4	5	6	7	8	9	10

July
Week 28

Saturday 15

Meal ideas

Sunday 16
(Last Quarter

Meal ideas

Cherry Cupcakes

V ❄

Time 30 mins   Makes 12 cakes
Calories 265 per portion
Fat 14g of which 8.5g is saturated

Butter 175g (6oz)
Caster sugar 110g (4oz)
Eggs 2, beaten
Self-raising flour 110g (4oz), sifted
Glacé cherries 50g (2oz), chopped
Icing sugar 110g (4oz)
White chocolate buttons and
Halved glacé cherries to decorate

1 Preheat oven to 190°C/170°fan/ Gas 5. Spread out 12 paper cases on baking sheets, or put them into patty tins.
2 Cream 110g (4oz) butter and all caster sugar together until pale and fluffy. Gradually beat in eggs, beating well after each addition. Fold in flour, then chopped cherries.
3 Fill paper cases half full and bake for 15–20 minutes, until golden. Transfer to a wire rack to cool.
4 Beat remaining butter with icing sugar for butter icing and spread over top of cooled cakes.
5 Decorate with white chocolate buttons and glacé cherries.

July
Week 29

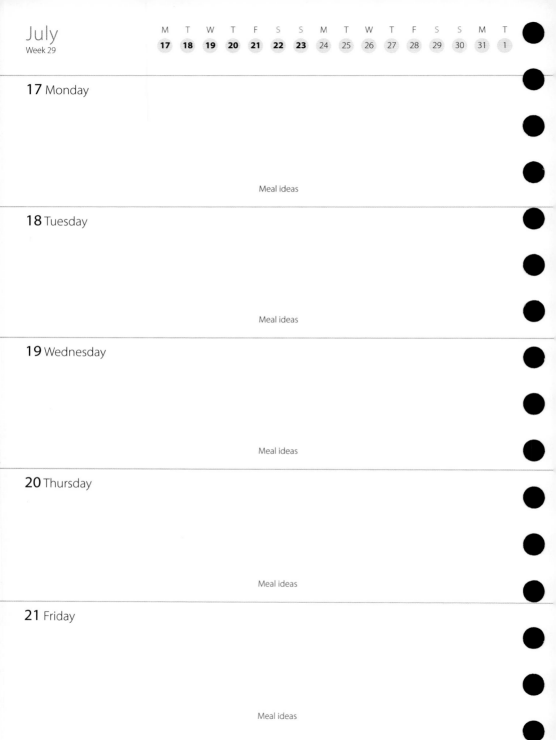

M T W T F S S M T W T F S S M T
17 18 19 20 21 22 23 24 25 26 27 28 29 30 31 1

17 Monday

Meal ideas

18 Tuesday

Meal ideas

19 Wednesday

Meal ideas

20 Thursday

Meal ideas

21 Friday

Meal ideas

Saturday 22

Meal ideas

Sunday 23
● New Moon

Meal ideas

Fruity Chicken Couscous

Couscous 200g (7oz)
Hot chicken or vegetable stock
300ml (½ pint)
Pine nuts 50g (2oz)
Skinless chicken breasts 2
Olive oil 3 tbsp
Mint 15g (½oz), chopped
Raisins 75g (3oz)
Lemon juice 2 tbsp

Time 22 mins   Serves 2
Calories 819 per portion
Fat 37g of which 5g is saturated

1 Put couscous in a large bowl, add stock, cover and leave for 5 minutes.
2 Heat a large frying pan, add pine nuts and toast for about 2 minutes. Tip over couscous.
3 Cut each chicken breast diagonally lengthways into 5 thin slices. Add 1 tbsp of oil to frying pan and heat. Add chicken pieces and cook for 3–4 minutes on each side until cooked through.
4 Meanwhile, add mint and raisins to couscous and season. Toss together.
5 Mix remaining olive oil in a small bowl with lemon juice. Spoon couscous onto serving plates, pile chicken slices on top and drizzle with lemon dressing to serve.

M T W T F S S S M T W T F S S M T
24 25 26 27 28 29 30 31 1 2 3 4 5 6 7 8

24 Monday

Meal ideas

25 Tuesday

Meal ideas

26 Wednesday

Meal ideas

27 Thursday

Meal ideas

28 Friday

Meal ideas

Saturday **29**

Meal ideas

Sunday **30**
☽ First Quarter

Meal ideas

Mixed Citrus Sorbet

V ❄

Lemons, limes and oranges 3 large of each
Caster sugar 350g (12oz)
Orange wedges to serve

1 Peel rinds from fruit. Squeeze fruit and strain juice.
2 Put rinds into a non-reactive saucepan with 750ml (1¼ pints) water and bring to the boil. Remove from heat and strain into a clean pan (discard rinds). Add sugar and stir over a moderate heat until dissolved.
3 Bring to the boil and boil for 2 minutes. Remove from heat, stir in juice, cover and when cool refrigerate for 1–2 hours.
4 Freeze mixture in ice cream machine or pour into a bowl and freeze until it starts to freeze at the edges. Whisk and return to freezer. Repeat until sorbet is almost frozen. Transfer to lidded freezer-proof container and freeze.
5 To serve, remove sorbet from freezer for 20 minutes, or until slightly softened. Serve decorated with orange wedges.

Time 1 hr plus freezing   Serves 8
Calories 183 per portion
Fat 0g of which 0g is saturated

31 Monday

Meal ideas

1 Tuesday August

Meal ideas

2 Wednesday

Meal ideas

3 Thursday

Meal ideas

4 Friday

Meal ideas

Saturday **5**

Meal ideas

Sunday **6**

Meal ideas

Florida Coleslaw

V

White cabbage 225g (8oz), finely shredded
Dessert apple 1, peeled, cored and grated
Carrot 1, peeled and grated
Raisins 25g (1oz)
Orange ¼, finely grated rind and juice
Natural yogurt 110g (4oz)
Light mayonnaise 2 tbsp
Lemon juice 2 tsp

1 Combine shredded cabbage with grated apple and carrot, raisins and orange rind and juice.
2 Add yogurt, mayonnaise, lemon juice and salt and freshly ground black pepper and toss well together.

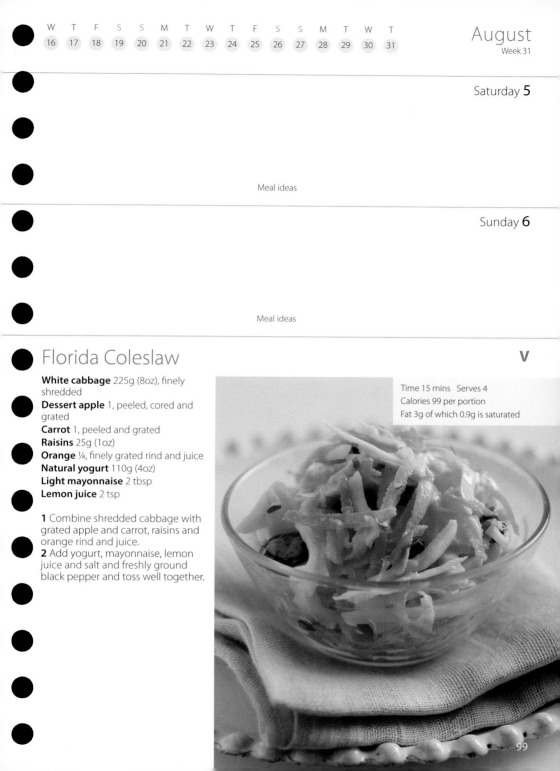

Time 15 mins   Serves 4
Calories 99 per portion
Fat 3g of which 0.9g is saturated

99

7 Monday
○ Full Moon

Bank Holiday, Scotland

Meal ideas

8 Tuesday

Meal ideas

9 Wednesday

Meal ideas

10 Thursday

Meal ideas

11 Friday

Meal ideas

W	T	F	S	S	M	T	W	T	F	S	S	M	T	W	T
23	24	25	26	27	28	29	30	31	1	2	3	4	5	6	7

August
Week 32

Saturday 12

Meal ideas

Sunday 13

Meal ideas

Caribbean Shake

V

Banana 1, chopped
Orange juice 2 tbsp
Pineapple juice 2 tbsp
Milk 300ml (½ pint)
Vanilla dairy ice cream 2 scoops

1 Put banana in a blender with orange and pineapple juices. Add milk and whizz to blend.
2 Put a scoop of ice cream in two glasses and top up with fruit milk. Serve immediately.

Time 5 mins   Serves 2
Calories 199 per glass
Fat 7g of which 4.2g is saturated

101

August
Week 33

M	T	W	T	F	S	S	M	T	W	T	F	S	S	M	T
14	**15**	**16**	**17**	**18**	**19**	**20**	21	22	23	24	25	26	27	28	29

14 Monday

Meal ideas

15 Tuesday
☾ Last Quarter

Meal ideas

16 Wednesday

Meal ideas

17 Thursday

Meal ideas

18 Friday

Meal ideas

W	T	F	S	S	M	T	W	T	F	S	S	M	T	W	T
30	31	1	2	3	4	5	6	7	8	9	10	11	12	13	14

August
Week 33

Saturday 19

Meal ideas

Sunday 20

Meal ideas

Veggie Crisps with Chive Dip

V

Vegetable oil for deep frying
Sweet potatoes 3 large, peeled
Parsnips 4 large, peeled
Carrots 4 large, peeled
Soured cream 150ml (¼ pint)
Finely snipped chives 2 tbsp
Sea salt for sprinkling

1 Heat vegetable oil in a large pan or deep fat fryer.
2 Using a vegetable peeler, slice all vegetables very thinly. Pat vegetables dry on kitchen paper.
3 Fry vegetable slices, in batches, until golden. Drain on kitchen paper.
4 Mix soured cream with chives. Sprinkle crisps with sea salt and serve with soured cream dip.

Time 1 hr   Serves 8
Calories 417 per portion
Fat 30g of which 5.4g is saturated

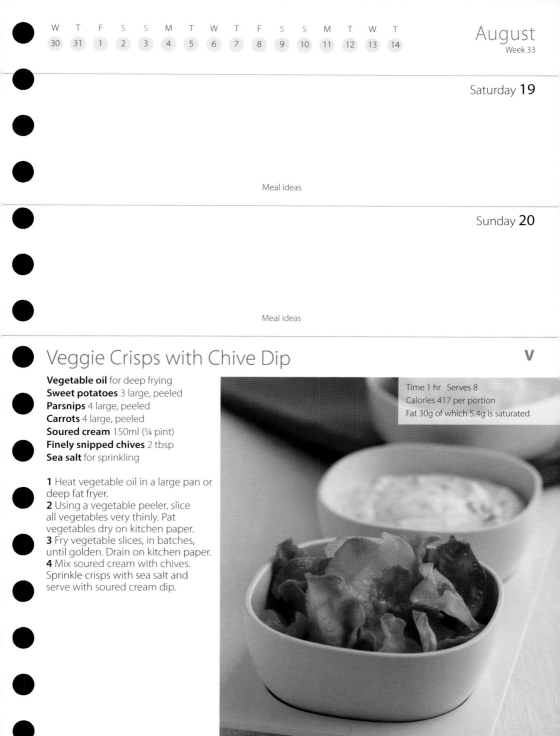

August
Week 34

21 Monday
● New Moon

Meal ideas

22 Tuesday

Meal ideas

23 Wednesday

Meal ideas

24 Thursday

Meal ideas

25 Friday

Meal ideas

Saturday **26**

Meal ideas

Sunday **27**

Meal ideas

Blueberry Baked Alaskas

V

Madeira cake cut into 4 x 7.5cm (3in) diameter circles, each 1cm (½in) thick
Rum or sherry 4 tbsp (optional)
Blueberries 110g (4oz)
Egg whites 3
Light soft brown sugar 175g (6oz)
Vanilla ice cream 4 scoops

1 Preheat oven to 220°C/200°fan/ Gas 7. Place Madeira cake slices on a baking sheet and, if using, drizzle 1 tbsp of rum or sherry over each slice.
2 Arrange blueberries in a circle on top of each cake slice, allowing a gap in middle for ice cream.
3 Whisk egg whites until stiff, gradually adding sugar and whisking until thick and glossy.
4 Place a scoop of ice cream centrally on each cake slice and cover with meringue mixture.
5 Bake in oven for 5 minutes or until slightly golden. Serve immediately.

Cook's tip For a delicious pour-over sauce, melt 12 dairy toffees in 175g (6oz) evaporated milk.

Time 20 mins   Serves 4
Calories 490 per portion
Fat 13g of which 7.6g is saturated

105

August
Week 35

28 Monday

Bank Holiday, England, Wales and N Ireland

Meal ideas

29 Tuesday

› First Quarter

Meal ideas

30 Wednesday

Meal ideas

31 Thursday

Meal ideas

1 Friday September

Meal ideas

Saturday **2**

Meal ideas

Sunday **3**

Meal ideas

Spanish Tortilla

V ❄

Butter 50g (2oz)
Red onion 1 small, peeled and thinly sliced
Garlic 1 clove, peeled and crushed
Red pepper 1 small, deseeded and thinly sliced
Courgette 1, sliced
Potatoes 2, peeled, diced and parboiled
Eggs 8, beaten and seasoned
Finely chopped parsley 2 tbsp

1 Preheat grill to high.
2 Melt butter in a 25cm (10in) non-stick frying pan and fry onion and garlic for 3–4 minutes until soft.
3 Add red pepper, courgette and potatoes and fry for 3–4 minutes until soft.
4 Spread out vegetables in pan and pour over eggs. Sprinkle with parsley and leave to cook over a low heat for 10–15 minutes or until set.
5 Finish off by placing under grill for 2 minutes until golden.

Time 35 mins   Serves 4
Calories 352 per portion
Fat 24.2g of which 10.2g is saturated

September

Week 36

4 Monday

Meal ideas

5 Tuesday

Meal ideas

6 Wednesday
○ Full Moon

Meal ideas

7 Thursday

Meal ideas

8 Friday

Meal ideas

Saturday **9**

Meal ideas

Sunday **10**

Meal ideas

Kedgeree

Smoked haddock 350g (12oz)
Milk 600ml (1 pint)
Basmati rice 225g (8oz)
Butter 25g (1oz)
Onion 1, peeled and finely chopped
Curry powder 1 tsp
Turmeric ½ tsp
Double cream 2 tbsp
Chopped parsley 2 tbsp
Egg 1, hard-boiled, shelled and quartered

1 Place haddock in a shallow pan and cover with milk. Bring to boil, reduce heat and leave to simmer for about 5 minutes, until cooked. Remove fish from milk and flake (reserving liquor).
2 Bring milk back to the boil, add rice and top up with extra water if needed. Cook for 12 minutes, then drain well.
3 In another pan, melt butter and fry onion for 3–4 minutes, until softened. Stir in spices and then cooked rice.
4 Add fish to rice mixture. Pour in double cream and heat through over a low heat. Sprinkle with parsley and garnish with egg.

Time 50 mins   Serves 2
Calories 859 per portion
Fat 28.7g of which 15.2g is saturated

109

September

Week 37

11 Monday

Meal ideas

12 Tuesday

Meal ideas

13 Wednesday
☾ Last Quarter

Meal ideas

14 Thursday

Meal ideas

15 Friday

Meal ideas

W	T	F	S	S	M	T	W	T	F	S	S	M	T	W	T
27	28	29	30	1	2	3	4	5	6	7	8	9	10	11	12

September
Week 37

Saturday **16**

Meal ideas

Sunday **17**

Meal ideas

Cheshire Cheese & Apple Pasties

V ❄

Puff pastry 300g (11oz), defrosted if frozen
Onion chutney 4 tsp
Cheshire cheese 110g (4oz), crumbled
Cox apple 1, peeled, cored and chopped
Chopped sage 1 tbsp
Egg 1, beaten

Time 30 mins   Serves 4
Calories 428 per portion
Fat 28g of which 12.9g is saturated

1 Preheat oven to 200°C/180°fan/Gas 6. Grease a baking tray. Roll out pastry and cut out 4 x 18cm (7in) circles. Spread the centre of each with chutney.
2 Mix cheese, apple and sage together and divide between pastry circles. Brush edge of each circle with water, fold in half and press to seal. Place on baking tray.
3 Prick pastry, brush with beaten egg and bake for 20-25 minutes until golden brown and crisp.

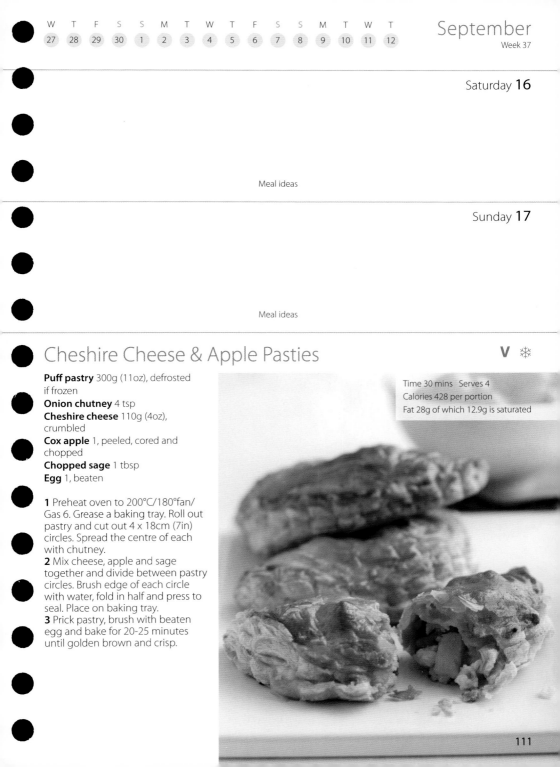

September
Week 38

M	T	W	T	F	S	S	M	T	W	T	F	S	S	M	T
18	**19**	**20**	**21**	**22**	**23**	**24**	25	26	27	28	29	30	1	2	3

18 Monday

Meal ideas

19 Tuesday

Meal ideas

20 Wednesday
● New Moon

Meal ideas

21 Thursday

Meal ideas

22 Friday
Autumnal equinox

Autumn begins

Meal ideas

Saturday **23**

Meal ideas

Sunday **24**

Meal ideas

Raspberry & Amaretti Trifle

V

Trifle sponges 4
Raspberry jam 2 tbsp
Sherry 4 tbsp
Amaretti biscuits 25g (1oz), crumbled
Raspberries 150g (5oz), plus extra to decorate
Double cream 300ml (½ pint)
Custard 425g can
Amaretto liqueur 2 tbsp (optional)

Time 20 mins   Serves 8
Calories 339 per portion
Fat 24g of which 13.4g is saturated

1 Halve trifle sponges and sandwich together with jam. Cut into quarters and arrange in a trifle dish.
2 Pour sherry over sponges and sprinkle with amaretti. Reserving a few raspberries for decoration, place remainder in dish.
3 Stir 3 tbsp cream into custard, then pour over fruit, cover and chill.
4 Whip remaining cream with liqueur, if using, until soft peaks form. Spread over custard and decorate with reserved raspberries.

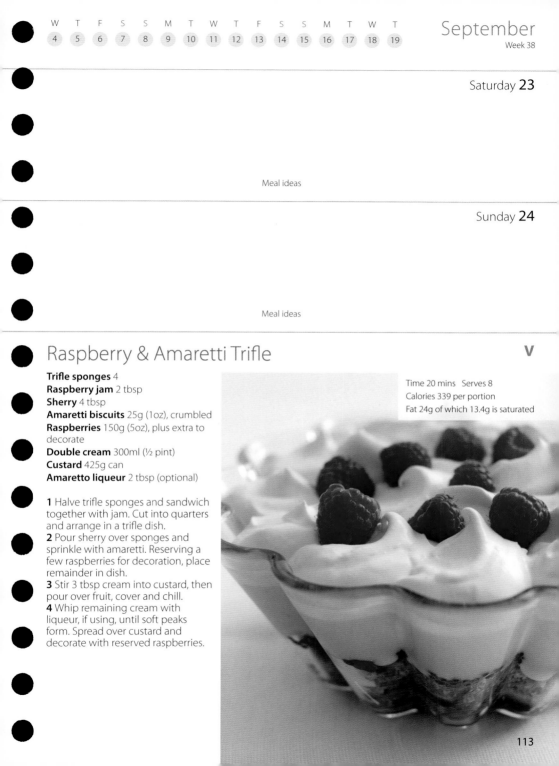

September

Week 39

25 Monday

Don't forget to order your 2018 Recipe Diary. Visit recipediary.co.uk

Meal ideas

26 Tuesday

Meal ideas

27 Wednesday

Meal ideas

28 Thursday

❯ First Quarter

Meal ideas

29 Friday

Meal ideas

Saturday 30

Meal ideas

October Sunday 1

Meal ideas

Potato Wedges with a Trio of Dips

V

Potatoes 6-8, scrubbed
Olive oil 4-6 tbsp
Tomato Dip
Tomatoes 4, deseeded and chopped
Mild red chilli ½, deseeded and chopped
Garlic 1 clove, peeled and crushed
Olive oil 2-3 tbsp
Avocado Dip
Avocados 2 ripe, peeled, stoned and mashed
Snipped chives 2 tbsp
Lime 1, finely grated zest and juice
Stilton Dip
Stilton 110g (4oz), crumbled
Half fat crème fraîche 200ml (7fl oz)

Time 50 mins   Serves 6-8
Calories 354 per portion
Fat 23g of which 8g is saturated

1 Preheat oven to 230°C/210°fan/Gas 8. Cut potatoes into eighths, toss in oil and sprinkle with salt and pepper. Spread out on a large baking sheet and cook for 30 minutes, turning frequently, and brushing with olive oil.
2 Combine ingredients for each dip in separate bowls and season to taste. Chill until required.
3 Serve hot potato wedges with the cool dips. Perfect for alfresco dining!

115

October

M	T	W	T	F	S	S	M	T	W	T	F	S	S	M	T
2	3	4	5	6	7	8	9	10	11	12	13	14	15	16	17

2 Monday

Meal ideas

3 Tuesday

Meal ideas

4 Wednesday

Meal ideas

5 Thursday

○ Full Moon

Meal ideas

6 Friday

Meal ideas

Saturday 7

Meal ideas

Sunday 8

Meal ideas

Win a Fabulous Crêpe Maker!

Everyone has their favourite: Lemon and sugar, banana and chocolate, ham and cheese.

But that's just pancakes and crêpes. The Breville® Crêpe Maker is for so much more. Indulge in quirky quesadillas, funky fajitas and brilliant blinis too.

The VTP130 crepe maker is a 30cm (12") wide circular aluminium cooking plate with a non-stick coating to make cleaning extra easy. The crepe maker boasts an impressive 1kw of power to provide maximum heat in just 4 minutes. Its variable temperature control with 5 different heat settings gives you complete control to heat to your requirements.

For a chance to win this must-have gadget visit

recipediary.co.uk/crepe-maker

Closing date 30 November 2017.

Enter now at recipediary.co.uk/crepe-maker

WIN

October
Week 41

9 Monday

Meal ideas

10 Tuesday

Meal ideas

11 Wednesday

Meal ideas

12 Thursday
☾ Last Quarter

Meal ideas

13 Friday

Meal ideas

W	T	F	S	S	M	T	W	T	F	S	S	M	T	W	T
25	26	27	28	29	30	31	1	2	3	4	5	6	7	8	9

October
Week 41

Saturday **14**

Meal ideas

Sunday **15**

Meal ideas

Mushrooms on Toast

Butter 50g (2oz), softened
Tomato paste 2 tbsp
Chestnut mushrooms 150g (5oz), wiped and halved
Closed cup mushrooms 200g (7oz), wiped
Snipped chives or chopped spring onion leaves 3 tbsp
Worcestershire sauce 2 tbsp
White or wholemeal bread 2 thick slices

Time 30 mins   Serves 2
Calories 318 per portion
Fat 22g of which 13.4g is saturated

1 In a small bowl, blend together 25g (1oz) of butter and the tomato paste.
2 Melt remaining butter in a frying pan, add mushrooms and chives or spring onion leaves and cook them over a moderate heat until mushrooms are only just cooked and lightly browned all over.
3 Add Worcestershire sauce to frying pan, increase heat to high and cook mushrooms briskly for a few minutes until juices are reduced by half to two-thirds (depending on the variety of mushrooms).
4 Meanwhile, toast bread and spread with tomato butter. Place on serving plates, add mushrooms and serve immediately.

Cook's tip Depending on what is available, such as chestnut and flat mushrooms, the blend of mushrooms can be varied to suit personal taste.

October
Week 42

16 Monday

Meal ideas

17 Tuesday

Meal ideas

18 Wednesday

Meal ideas

19 Thursday
● New Moon

Meal ideas

20 Friday

Meal ideas

W	T	F	S	S	M	T	W	T	F	S	S	M	T	W	T
1	2	3	4	5	6	7	8	9	10	11	12	13	14	15	16

October
Week 42

Saturday 21

Meal ideas

Sunday 22

Meal ideas

Cappuccino Cakes

V ❄

Self-raising flour 175g (6oz), sifted
Butter 110g (4oz), at room temperature
Caster sugar 110g (4oz)
Eggs 2 large, beaten
Milk 2 tbsp
Instant coffee 2 tsp, dissolved in 1 tsp boiling water
Cocoa powder 25g (1oz)
Double cream 150ml (¼ pint)
Icing sugar 1 tbsp
Milk chocolate curls made with a swivel-bladed vegetable peeler run along underside of chocolate bar

Time 35 mins   Makes 12 cakes
Calories 261 per portion
Fat 17.2g of which 9.7g is saturated

1 Preheat oven to 180°C/160°fan/Gas 4.
2 In a large bowl, add flour, butter, caster sugar, eggs, milk, coffee and cocoa powder with a pinch of salt. Beat together until mixture is smooth and has a dropping consistency.
3 Divide mixture between 12 paper cases sitting in a patty tin. Bake in oven for 15 minutes until well risen, then leave to cool on a wire rack.
4 Whisk together cream and icing sugar. Pipe or spoon the cream on top of cooled cakes and sprinkle with chocolate curls.

121

October

23 Monday

Meal ideas

24 Tuesday

Meal ideas

25 Wednesday

Meal ideas

26 Thursday

Meal ideas

27 Friday
❭ First Quarter

Meal ideas

Saturday 28

Don't forget to put your clocks back 1 hour tonight

Meal ideas

Sunday 29

British Summer Time ends

Veggie Moussaka

V ❄

Olive oil 4 tbsp
Aubergines 350g (12oz), thinly sliced
Potatoes 350g (12oz), peeled, cooked for about 15 minutes and sliced
Vegetables e.g. courgettes, onions, peppers 500g (1lb 2oz), sliced
Garlic 2 cloves, peeled and crushed
Vegetable stock 150ml (¼ pint)
Tomato purée 2 tbsp
Oregano 2 tbsp, or 1 tsp dried
Milk 300ml (½ pint)
Butter 25g (1oz)
Plain flour 25g (1oz)
Cheddar cheese 75g (3oz), grated
Egg 1, beaten

Time 1½ hrs   Serves 4
Calories 427 per portion
Fat 26.9g of which 10.2g is saturated

1 Preheat oven to 180°C/160°fan/Gas 4. Heat 1 tbsp of oil and fry some of the aubergine for 2–3 minutes each side until softened and turning golden. Lift out and fry the rest in two batches, adding 1 tbsp oil each time. Arrange half of aubergine and potato in dish.
2 Sauté vegetables in remaining oil for 5 minutes. Add garlic, stock, tomato purée and oregano and simmer for 2–3 minutes. Spoon into dish and top with remaining aubergine and potato.
3 In a saucepan, bring milk, butter and flour to boil, stirring continuously. Add cheese, cook for 3 minutes, then add egg. Pour over potatoes. Bake for 40–45 minutes until golden.

M T W T F S S M T W T F S S M T
30 **31** **1** **2** **3** **4** **5** 6 7 8 9 10 11 12 13 14

30 Monday

Meal ideas

31 Tuesday
Halloween

Meal ideas

1 Wednesday November

Meal ideas

2 Thursday

Meal ideas

3 Friday

Meal ideas

Saturday **4**
◯ Full Moon

Meal ideas

Sunday **5**
Bonfire Night

Meal ideas

Halloween Cake Pops **v**

Madeira cake 285g loaf
Full fat soft cheese 125g (4½oz)
Orange chocolate buttons 100g packet
White chocolate 110g (4oz), chopped
Orange sugar sprinkles, popping candy and sugar stars to decorate

Time 35 mins Makes 18–20
Calories 127 per portion
Fat 7g of which 4.1g is saturated

1 Crumble cake to crumbs into a bowl. Beat in cheese and squeeze together with your fingers.
2 Roll cake mix into 18-20 even-sized balls about the size of a walnut. Meanwhile, melt chocolate in two separate heatproof bowls over barely simmering water, making sure the bottom of the bowl does not touch the water. Remove from heat. Dip end of 18-20 15cm (6in) lollipop sticks in a little chocolate and stick into each cake pop.
3 Drizzle half the pops with orange chocolate. Then drizzle the other pops with white chocolate. Let excess chocolate drain off then place into a glass to dry.
4 Just before they're set, sprinkle with decorations. Leave to set and enjoy the same day.

125

November
Week 45

M	T	W	T	F	S	S	M	T	W	T	F	S	S	M	T
6	7	8	9	10	11	12	13	14	15	16	17	18	19	20	21

6 Monday

Meal ideas

7 Tuesday

Meal ideas

8 Wednesday

Meal ideas

9 Thursday

Meal ideas

10 Friday
☾ Last Quarter

Meal ideas

Saturday 11

Meal ideas

Sunday 12
Remembrance Sunday

Meal ideas

Cinnamon Toast

V

Light soft brown sugar 4 tbsp
Cinnamon 1 tsp
Butter 50g (2oz), softened
White bread 6 slices

1 Mix sugar with cinnamon and softened butter. Toast bread slices on both sides.
2 Spread one side of toast with butter mixture, cut in half and serve.

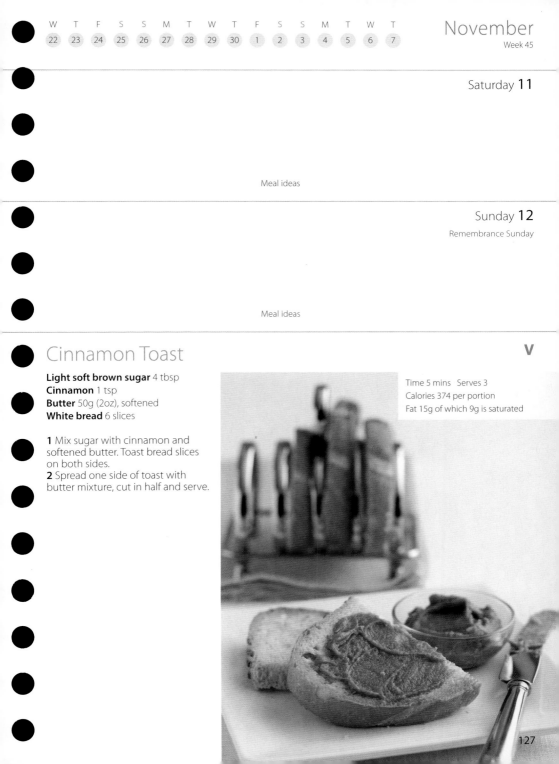

Time 5 mins   Serves 3
Calories 374 per portion
Fat 15g of which 9g is saturated

127

November

Week 46

13 Monday

Meal ideas

14 Tuesday

Meal ideas

15 Wednesday

Meal ideas

16 Thursday

Meal ideas

17 Friday

Meal ideas

W	T	F	S	S	M	T	W	T	F	S	S	M	T	W	T
29	30	1	2	3	4	5	6	7	8	9	10	11	12	13	14

November
Week 46

Saturday **18**
● New Moon

Meal ideas

Sunday **19**

Meal ideas

Pork Chops with Cheddar & Apple

Mushrooms 110g (4oz), sliced
Cooking apples 2, peeled, cored and sliced
Onion 1, peeled and sliced
Pork loin chops 4
Apple juice 300ml (½ pint)
Dry breadcrumbs 50g (2oz)
Cheddar cheese 110g (4oz), grated
Green beans to serve (optional)

Time 1½–1¾ hrs   Serves 4
Calories 618 per portion
Fat 41g of which 18.1g is saturated

1 Preheat oven to 200°C/180°fan/ Gas 6. Butter a 1.7 litre (3 pint) shallow ovenproof dish. Place mushrooms, apples and onion in base of dish and season with salt and freshly ground black pepper.
2 Place pork chops on top and cover with apple juice. Mix breadcrumbs and cheese together and sprinkle over chops.
3 Bake in oven for 1¼–1½ hours (covering with foil after 45 minutes to stop overbrowning), until chops are cooked. Serve with green beans, if using.

November

Week 47

M	T	W	T	F	S	S	M	T	W	T	F	S	S	M	T
20	**21**	**22**	**23**	**24**	**25**	**26**	27	28	29	30	1	2	3	4	5

20 Monday

Meal ideas

21 Tuesday

Meal ideas

22 Wednesday

Meal ideas

23 Thursday

Meal ideas

24 Friday

Meal ideas

W	T	F	S	S	M	T	W	T	F	S	S	M	T	W	T
6	7	8	9	10	11	12	13	14	15	16	17	18	19	20	21

November
Week 47

Saturday 25

Meal ideas

Sunday 26
) First Quarter

Meal ideas

Fruity Winter Warmer

V

Frozen mixed summer fruits 400g packet
Soft light brown sugar 175g (6oz)
Cinnamon stick 5cm (2in) piece
Fresh apple juice 1 litre carton
Apple, orange, lemon and pear 1 of each, cored and sliced

1 Put frozen fruits into a pan, add sugar, cinnamon stick and 600ml (1 pint) water. Heat gently for 20–25 minutes, or until fruits are very soft.
2 Place a sieve over a large bowl, then pour fruits into the sieve and allow to drain. Gently press down on fruits to extract all of the juice but do not pass pulp through sieve.
3 Pour strained juice back into the pan. Add apple juice and sliced fruits and heat gently until hot, but not boiling. Serve juice and sliced fruit in heat-resistant glasses or mugs.

Time 45 mins   Serves 6
Calories 224 per portion
Fat 0g of which 0g is saturated

131

M	T	W	T	F	S	S	M	T	W	T	F	S	S	M	T
27	28	29	30	1	2	3	4	5	6	7	8	9	10	11	12

27 Monday

Meal ideas

28 Tuesday

Meal ideas

29 Wednesday

Meal ideas

30 Thursday
St Andrew's Day

Meal ideas

1 Friday December

Meal ideas

W	T	F	S	S	M	T	W	T	F	S	S	M	T	W	T
13	14	15	16	17	18	19	20	21	22	23	24	25	26	27	28

December
Week 48

Saturday 2

Meal ideas

Sunday 3
○ Full Moon

Meal ideas

Rich Creamy Porridge with Raspberries   V

Jumbo porridge oats 75g (3oz)
Milk 300ml (½ pint)
Single cream 300ml (½ pint)
Raspberries 110g (4oz)
Honey to serve

Time 20 mins   Serves 3
Calories 344 per portion
Fat 22g of which 13g is saturated

1 Tip oats, milk and cream into a large heavy-based pan and bring slowly to the boil, stirring often. Reduce heat to a simmer and cook gently for 10-15 minutes or until porridge is tender and thickened.
2 Spoon into small bowls. Add a few raspberries and a drizzle of honey and serve.

133

4 Monday

Meal ideas

5 Tuesday

Meal ideas

6 Wednesday

Meal ideas

7 Thursday

Meal ideas

8 Friday

Meal ideas

Saturday 9

Meal ideas

Sunday 10
☾ Last Quarter

Meal ideas

Calypso Puddings

V ❄

Pitted prunes 200g (7oz), roughly chopped
Lemon and orange 1 of each, grated zest and juice
White or dark rum 4 tbsp
Soft dark brown sugar 50g (2oz)
Eggs 3, beaten
Ready-to-eat dried apricots 110g (4oz), roughly chopped
Raisins and sultanas 150g (5oz) of each
Freshly prepared mango and pineapple flesh 110g (4oz) of each, cut into 1cm (½in) cubes
Maraschino cherries 110g (4oz), drained and quartered
Wholemeal breadcrumbs 200g (7oz)
Pineapple slices 4, cut into wedges to serve (optional)

Time 3½ hours Makes 8
Calories 348 per portion
Fat 4g of which 0.9g is saturated

1 Grease 8 x 200ml (7fl oz) pudding moulds and base line with baking paper. Cut 8 larger rounds from baking paper and foil for covering.
2 Put all ingredients except pineapple slices into a large bowl. Mix well, spoon into moulds and smooth tops. Place larger paper rounds on top and cover securely with foil.
3 Steam puddings for 2 hours. When ready to serve, turn puddings out and serve with pineapple slices, if using.

Cook's tip Puddings can be prepared and cooked 6-8 weeks before Christmas and then steamed for 45 minutes to reheat on the day.

135

December
Week 50

11 Monday

Meal ideas

12 Tuesday

Meal ideas

13 Wednesday

Meal ideas

14 Thursday

Meal ideas

15 Friday

Meal ideas

W	T	F	S	S	M	T	W	T	F	S	S	M	T	W	T
27	28	29	30	31	1	2	3	4	5	6	7	8	9	10	11

December
Week 50

Saturday 16

Meal ideas

Sunday 17

Meal ideas

Chestnut Soup

V ❄

Butter 15g (½oz)
Onion 1 large, peeled and chopped
Frozen peeled chestnuts 500g packet
Vegetable stock 1 litre (1¾ pints)
Mixed dried herbs 1½ tsp
Single or double cream and paprika to garnish (optional)

1 Melt butter in a large saucepan, add onion and cook gently for 5 minutes until softened, taking care not to let it brown.
2 Add chestnuts, vegetable stock and herbs and bring to the boil. Reduce heat, cover and cook gently for 30 minutes, or until chestnuts have softened.
3 Purée with a stick blender and season to taste.
4 To serve, reheat and garnish with a swirl of double cream and a light sifting of paprika, if using.

Time 45 mins   Serves 4
Calories 279 per portion
Fat 7g of which 2.6g is saturated

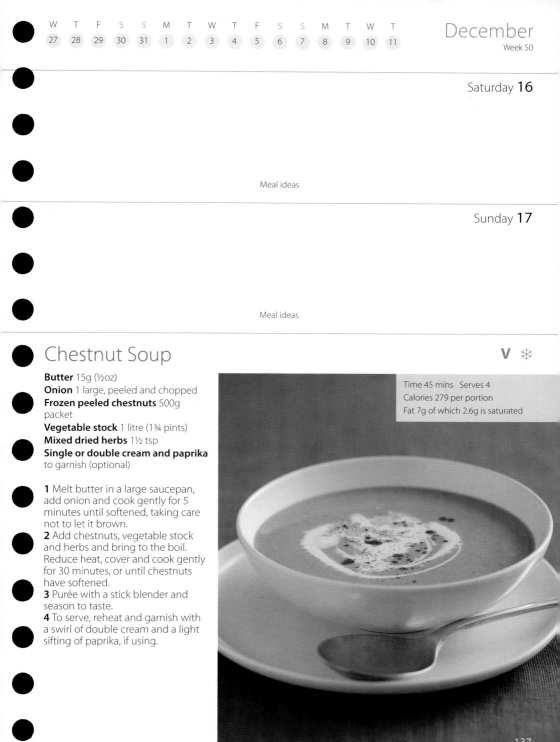

137

December

Week 51

18 Monday
● New Moon

Meal ideas

19 Tuesday

Meal ideas

20 Wednesday

Meal ideas

21 Thursday

Winter solstice

Winter begins

Meal ideas

22 Friday

Meal ideas

Saturday 23

Meal ideas

Sunday 24

Christmas Eve

Meal ideas

Festive Ice Cream

V ❄

Mixed dried fruit 110g (4oz)
Dark rum 4 tbsp
Port 2 tbsp
Single cream 450ml (¾ pint)
Egg yolks 3
Caster sugar 110g (4oz)
Whipping cream 150ml (¼ pint)
Orange 1, finely grated zest only
Mixed spice ½ tsp
Biscuits to serve (optional)

Time 30 mins, plus soaking and
freezing time   Serves 6
Calories 431 per portion
Fat 28g of which 16.1g is saturated

1 Mix dried fruit, rum and port in a
bowl. Cover and leave for 5 hours.
2 Gently heat single cream to
simmering point.
3 Beat yolks and sugar until pale
and fluffy. Add hot cream, stirring.
Strain into a heavy pan and stir over
a gentle heat until custard coats the
back of a wooden spoon. Cool by
standing pan in a bowl of cold water
and stirring custard continuously.
4 Whip cream until it forms soft
swirls. Fold into custard with fruit,
orange zest and mixed spice. Pour
into a container and freeze. Beat
mixture twice at hourly intervals
then cover, seal and freeze. Serve
with biscuits on the side, if using.

25 Monday
Christmas Day

Bank Holiday, UK

Meal ideas

26 Tuesday
) First Quarter

Boxing Day

Bank Holiday, UK

Meal ideas

27 Wednesday

Meal ideas

28 Thursday

Meal ideas

29 Friday

Meal ideas

W	T	F	S	S	M	T	W	T	F	S	S	M	T	W	T
10	11	12	13	14	15	16	17	18	19	20	21	22	23	24	25

December
Week 52

Saturday **30**

Meal ideas

Sunday **31**
New Year's Eve

Meal ideas

Turkey Toasts with Cranberry Sauce

Butter 25g (1oz)
Plain flour 25g (1oz)
Chicken stock 300ml (½ pint)
Double or single cream 3 tbsp
Snipped chives 3 tbsp, plus a few leaves
Cooked turkey 1 thick slice, about 200g (7oz), chopped
Mayonnaise 2 tbsp
White sliced cob loaf 4 slices
Red Leicester cheese 110g (4oz), grated
Cranberry sauce 4 tbsp

1 Melt butter in a pan, stir in flour, add stock and bring to the boil, stirring continuously. Reduce heat and simmer for 2–3 minutes.
2 Mix cream, chives, turkey and mayonnaise into sauce.
3 Lightly toast bread on both sides, spread turkey mixture on top, put back on grill rack and sprinkle with cheese. Return to grill and heat just until cheese melts.
4 Garnish turkey toasts with chives and serve on warmed plates with the cranberry sauce in a bowl on the side.

Cook's tip This supper dish can also be made from leftover chicken or chicken breasts poached in chicken stock – using stock to make sauce.

Time 30 mins   Serves 4
Calories 483 per portion
Fat 29g of which 13.9g is saturated

141

January 2018
Week 1

M	T	W	T	F	S	S	M	T	W	T	F	S	S	M	T
1	2	3	4	5	6	7	8	9	10	11	12	13	14	15	16

1 Monday

New Year's Day
Bank Holiday, UK

2 Tuesday

Bank Holiday, Scotland

3 Wednesday

4 Thursday

5 Friday

Notes

Notes

Thoughts and plans for 2017

Thoughts and plans for 2018

Home budgeting

Opening balance

Income

New balance

Notes

Birthdays/Christmas	
Car insurance	
Car MOT/service/tax	
Childcare	
Clothing/shoes	
Council tax	
Dentist/optician	
Electricity	
Entertainment	
Gas/oil/solid fuel	
Groceries	
Hairdresser	
Holidays	
Home/pet insurance	
Life/medical insurance	
Mobile/phone/internet	
Mortgage/rent	
Newspapers/magazines	
Petrol/fares	
Pets	
Savings	
TV licence/satellite	
Water rates	
Other	
Other	
Other	
Other	
Other	
Other	
Other	

Total expenditure

Closing balance

February

	Opening balance	
	Income	
	New balance	

	Notes
Birthdays/Christmas	
Car insurance	
Car MOT/service/tax	
Childcare	
Clothing/shoes	
Council tax	
Dentist/optician	
Electricity	
Entertainment	
Gas/oil/solid fuel	
Groceries	
Hairdresser	
Holidays	
Home/pet insurance	
Life/medical insurance	
Mobile/phone/internet	
Mortgage/rent	
Newspapers/magazines	
Petrol/fares	
Pets	
Savings	
TV licence/satellite	
Water rates	
Other	
Other	
Other	
Other	
Other	
Other	
Other	

	Total expenditure	
	Closing balance	

March

Opening balance
Income
New balance

Notes

Birthdays/Christmas	
Car insurance	
Car MOT/service/tax	
Childcare	
Clothing/shoes	
Council tax	
Dentist/optician	
Electricity	
Entertainment	
Gas/oil/solid fuel	
Groceries	
Hairdresser	
Holidays	
Home/pet insurance	
Life/medical insurance	
Mobile/phone/internet	
Mortgage/rent	
Newspapers/magazines	
Petrol/fares	
Pets	
Savings	
TV licence/satellite	
Water rates	
Other	
Other	
Other	
Other	
Other	
Other	
Other	

Total expenditure

Closing balance

April

	Opening balance	
	Income	
	New balance	

Notes	
Birthdays/Christmas	
Car insurance	
Car MOT/service/tax	
Childcare	
Clothing/shoes	
Council tax	
Dentist/optician	
Electricity	
Entertainment	
Gas/oil/solid fuel	
Groceries	
Hairdresser	
Holidays	
Home/pet insurance	
Life/medical insurance	
Mobile/phone/internet	
Mortgage/rent	
Newspapers/magazines	
Petrol/fares	
Pets	
Savings	
TV licence/satellite	
Water rates	
Other	
Other	
Other	
Other	
Other	
Other	
Other	

	Total expenditure	
	Closing balance	

May

	Opening balance	
	Income	
	New balance	

Notes	
Birthdays/Christmas	
Car insurance	
Car MOT/service/tax	
Childcare	
Clothing/shoes	
Council tax	
Dentist/optician	
Electricity	
Entertainment	
Gas/oil/solid fuel	
Groceries	
Hairdresser	
Holidays	
Home/pet insurance	
Life/medical insurance	
Mobile/phone/internet	
Mortgage/rent	
Newspapers/magazines	
Petrol/fares	
Pets	
Savings	
TV licence/satellite	
Water rates	
Other	
Other	
Other	
Other	
Other	
Other	
Other	

	Total expenditure	
	Closing balance	

Opening balance

Income

New balance

Notes

Birthdays/Christmas	
Car insurance	
Car MOT/service/tax	
Childcare	
Clothing/shoes	
Council tax	
Dentist/optician	
Electricity	
Entertainment	
Gas/oil/solid fuel	
Groceries	
Hairdresser	
Holidays	
Home/pet insurance	
Life/medical insurance	
Mobile/phone/internet	
Mortgage/rent	
Newspapers/magazines	
Petrol/fares	
Pets	
Savings	
TV licence/satellite	
Water rates	
Other	
Other	
Other	
Other	
Other	
Other	
Other	

Total expenditure

Closing balance

July

Opening balance	
Income	
New balance	

Notes

Birthdays/Christmas	
Car insurance	
Car MOT/service/tax	
Childcare	
Clothing/shoes	
Council tax	
Dentist/optician	
Electricity	
Entertainment	
Gas/oil/solid fuel	
Groceries	
Hairdresser	
Holidays	
Home/pet insurance	
Life/medical insurance	
Mobile/phone/internet	
Mortgage/rent	
Newspapers/magazines	
Petrol/fares	
Pets	
Savings	
TV licence/satellite	
Water rates	
Other	
Other	
Other	
Other	
Other	
Other	
Other	

Total expenditure	
Closing balance	

August

	Opening balance	
	Income	
	New balance	

Notes	
Birthdays/Christmas	
Car insurance	
Car MOT/service/tax	
Childcare	
Clothing/shoes	
Council tax	
Dentist/optician	
Electricity	
Entertainment	
Gas/oil/solid fuel	
Groceries	
Hairdresser	
Holidays	
Home/pet insurance	
Life/medical insurance	
Mobile/phone/internet	
Mortgage/rent	
Newspapers/magazines	
Petrol/fares	
Pets	
Savings	
TV licence/satellite	
Water rates	
Other	
Other	
Other	
Other	
Other	
Other	
Other	

	Total expenditure	
	Closing balance	

September

	Opening balance	
	Income	
	New balance	

Notes

Birthdays/Christmas	
Car insurance	
Car MOT/service/tax	
Childcare	
Clothing/shoes	
Council tax	
Dentist/optician	
Electricity	
Entertainment	
Gas/oil/solid fuel	
Groceries	
Hairdresser	
Holidays	
Home/pet insurance	
Life/medical insurance	
Mobile/phone/internet	
Mortgage/rent	
Newspapers/magazines	
Petrol/fares	
Pets	
Savings	
TV licence/satellite	
Water rates	
Other	
Other	
Other	
Other	
Other	
Other	
Other	

	Total expenditure	
	Closing balance	

October

	Opening balance	
	Income	
	New balance	

	Notes	
Birthdays/Christmas		
Car insurance		
Car MOT/service/tax		
Childcare		
Clothing/shoes		
Council tax		
Dentist/optician		
Electricity		
Entertainment		
Gas/oil/solid fuel		
Groceries		
Hairdresser		
Holidays		
Home/pet insurance		
Life/medical insurance		
Mobile/phone/internet		
Mortgage/rent		
Newspapers/magazines		
Petrol/fares		
Pets		
Savings		
TV licence/satellite		
Water rates		
Other		
Other		
Other		
Other		
Other		
Other		
Other		

| | Total expenditure | |
| | Closing balance | |

November

Opening balance		
Income		
New balance		

Birthdays/Christmas	
Car insurance	
Car MOT/service/tax	
Childcare	
Clothing/shoes	
Council tax	
Dentist/optician	
Electricity	
Entertainment	
Gas/oil/solid fuel	
Groceries	
Hairdresser	
Holidays	
Home/pet insurance	
Life/medical insurance	
Mobile/phone/internet	
Mortgage/rent	
Newspapers/magazines	
Petrol/fares	
Pets	
Savings	
TV licence/satellite	
Water rates	
Other	
Other	
Other	
Other	
Other	
Other	
Other	

Total expenditure		
Closing balance		

December

Opening balance

Income

New balance

Notes

Birthdays/Christmas	
Car insurance	
Car MOT/service/tax	
Childcare	
Clothing/shoes	
Council tax	
Dentist/optician	
Electricity	
Entertainment	
Gas/oil/solid fuel	
Groceries	
Hairdresser	
Holidays	
Home/pet insurance	
Life/medical insurance	
Mobile/phone/internet	
Mortgage/rent	
Newspapers/magazines	
Petrol/fares	
Pets	
Savings	
TV licence/satellite	
Water rates	
Other	
Other	
Other	
Other	
Other	
Other	
Other	

Total expenditure

Closing balance

Birthdays and anniversaries

Name	Celebration	Date

Weddings

1	Paper	14	Ivory
2	Cotton	15	Crystal
3	Leather	20	China
4	Books	25	Silver
5	Wood	30	Pearl
6	Iron	35	Coral
7	Wool	40	Ruby
8	Bronze	45	Sapphire
9	Copper	50	Gold
10	Tin	55	Emerald
11	Steel	60	Diamond
12	Silk or linen	65	Blue
13	Lace		Sapphire

Birthstones and flowers

Month	Birthstone	Flower
January	Garnet	Carnation
February	Amethyst	Violet
March	Aquamarine	Jonquil
April	Diamond	Sweet Pea
May	Emerald	Lily of the Valley
June	Pearl	Rose
July	Ruby	Larkspur
August	Peridot	Gladiolus
September	Sapphire	Aster
October	Opal	Calendula
November	Topaz	Chrysanthemum
December	Turquoise	Narcissus

Name	Celebration	Date

Year planner 2018

January		February	March
1 Mon	BANK HOLIDAY	1 Thu	1 Thu
2 Tue	BANK HOLIDAY SCOTLAND	2 Fri	2 Fri
3 Wed		3 Sat	3 Sat
4 Thu		4 Sun	4 Sun
5 Fri		5 Mon	5 Mon
6 Sat		6 Tue	6 Tue
7 Sun		7 Wed	7 Wed
8 Mon		8 Thu	8 Thu
9 Tue		9 Fri	9 Fri
10 Wed		10 Sat	10 Sat
11 Thu		11 Sun	11 Sun
12 Fri		12 Mon	12 Mon
13 Sat		13 Tue	13 Tue
14 Sun		14 Wed	14 Wed
15 Mon		15 Thu	15 Thu
16 Tue		16 Fri	16 Fri
17 Wed		17 Sat	17 Sat
18 Thu		18 Sun	18 Sun
19 Fri		19 Mon	19 Mon BANK HOLIDAY N IRELAND
20 Sat		20 Tue	20 Tue
21 Sun		21 Wed	21 Wed
22 Mon		22 Thu	22 Thu
23 Tue		23 Fri	23 Fri
24 Wed		24 Sat	24 Sat
25 Thu		25 Sun	25 Sun
26 Fri		26 Mon	26 Mon
27 Sat		27 Tue	27 Tue
28 Sun		28 Wed	28 Wed
29 Mon			29 Thu
30 Tues			30 Fri BANK HOLIDAY
31 Wed			31 Sat

April		May		June	
1 Sun		1 Tue		1 Fri	
2 Mon	BANK HOLIDAY	2 Wed		2 Sat	
3 Tue		3 Thu		3 Sun	
4 Wed		4 Fri		4 Mon	
5 Thu		5 Sat		5 Tue	
6 Fri		6 Sun		6 Wed	
7 Sat		7 Mon	BANK HOLIDAY	7 Thu	
8 Sun		8 Tue		8 Fri	
9 Mon		9 Wed		9 Sat	
10 Tue		10 Thu		10 Sun	
11 Wed		11 Fri		11 Mon	
12 Thu		12 Sat		12 Tue	
13 Fri		13 Sun		13 Wed	
14 Sat		14 Mon		14 Thu	
15 Sun		15 Tue		15 Fri	
16 Mon		16 Wed		16 Sat	
17 Tue		17 Thu		17 Sun	
18 Wed		18 Fri		18 Mon	
19 Thu		19 Sat		19 Tue	
20 Fri		20 Sun		20 Wed	
21 Sat		21 Mon		21 Thu	
22 Sun		22 Tue		22 Fri	
23 Mon		23 Wed		23 Sat	
24 Tue		24 Thu		24 Sun	
25 Wed		25 Fri		25 Mon	
26 Thu		26 Sat		26 Tue	
27 Fri		27 Sun		27 Wed	
28 Sat		28 Mon	BANK HOLIDAY	28 Thu	
29 Sun		29 Tue		29 Fri	
30 Mon		30 Wed		30 Sat	
		31 Thu			

Year planner 2018

July		August		September	
1	Sun	1	Wed	1	Sat
2	Mon	2	Thu	2	Sun
3	Tue	3	Fri	3	Mon
4	Wed	4	Sat	4	Tue
5	Thu	5	Sun	5	Wed
6	Fri	6	Mon BANK HOLIDAY SCOTLAND	6	Thu
7	Sat	7	Tue	7	Fri
8	Sun	8	Wed	8	Sat
9	Mon	9	Thu	9	Sun
10	Tue	10	Fri	10	Mon
11	Wed	11	Sat	11	Tue
12	Thu BANK HOLIDAY N IRELAND	12	Sun	12	Wed
13	Fri	13	Mon	13	Thu
14	Sat	14	Tue	14	Fri
15	Sun	15	Wed	15	Sat
16	Mon	16	Thu	16	Sun
17	Tue	17	Fri	17	Mon
18	Wed	18	Sat	18	Tue
19	Thu	19	Sun	19	Wed
20	Fri	20	Mon	20	Thu
21	Sat	21	Tue	21	Fri
22	Sun	22	Wed	22	Sat
23	Mon	23	Thu	23	Sun
24	Tue	24	Fri	24	Mon
25	Wed	25	Sat	25	Tue
26	Thu	26	Sun	26	Wed
27	Fri	27	Mon BANK HOLIDAY	27	Thu
28	Sat	28	Tue	28	Fri
29	Sun	29	Wed	29	Sat
30	Mon	30	Thu	30	Sun
31	Tue	31	Fri		

October	November	December	
1 Mon	1 Thu	1 Sat	
2 Tue	2 Fri	2 Sun	
3 Wed	3 Sat	3 Mon	
4 Thu	4 Sun	4 Tue	
5 Fri	5 Mon	5 Wed	
6 Sat	6 Tue	6 Thu	
7 Sun	7 Wed	7 Fri	
8 Mon	8 Thu	8 Sat	
9 Tue	9 Fri	9 Sun	
10 Wed	10 Sat	10 Mon	
11 Thu	11 Sun	11 Tue	
12 Fri	12 Mon	12 Wed	
13 Sat	13 Tue	13 Thu	
14 Sun	14 Wed	14 Fri	
15 Mon	15 Thu	15 Sat	
16 Tue	16 Fri	16 Sun	
17 Wed	17 Sat	17 Mon	
18 Thu	18 Sun	18 Tue	
19 Fri	19 Mon	19 Wed	
20 Sat	20 Tue	20 Thu	
21 Sun	21 Wed	21 Fri	
22 Mon	22 Thu	22 Sat	
23 Tue	23 Fri	23 Sun	
24 Wed	24 Sat	24 Mon	
25 Thu	25 Sun	25 Tue	BANK HOLIDAY
26 Fri	26 Mon	26 Wed	BANK HOLIDAY
27 Sat	27 Tue	27 Thu	
28 Sun	28 Wed	28 Fri	
29 Mon	29 Thu	29 Sat	
30 Tue	30 Fri	30 Sun	
31 Wed		31 Mon	

Recipe index

Visit **recipediary.co.uk** for more recipes.